Principles of Development and Differentiation

Cover photo is of a developing muscle fiber in a newt embryo, by the author.

CURRENT CONCEPTS IN BIOLOGY

A Macmillan Series

EDITORS: NORMAN H. GILES, WALTER KENWORTHY, AND JOHN G. TORREY

Initial Volumes in This Series

Algae and Fungi

C. J. Alexopoulos and H. C. Bold, The University of Texas

Sensory Mechanisms

James Case, University of California, Santa Barbara

Integral Animal Behavior

David E. Davis, The Pennsylvania State University

Molecular Genetics

A. Gib DeBusk, Florida State University

Biology of Higher Cryptogams

William T. Doyle, University of California, Santa Cruz

Viruses and Molecular Biology

Dean Fraser, Indiana University

Hormonal Control in Vertebrates

B. E. Frye, The University of Michigan

Cells and Energy

Richard A. Goldsby, Yale University

The Physiology of Cells

Karl F. Guthe, The University of Michigan

Process and Pattern in Evolution

Terrell H. Hamilton, The University of Texas

Tools of Biology

Edward S. Lenhoff, Harvard University

A Biology of Lower Invertebrates

W. D. Russell Hunter, Syracuse University

Animal Morphogenesis

John W. Saunders, Jr., University of Pennsylvania

Evolution and Systematics

Otto T. Solbrig, The University of Michigan

Development in Flowering Plants

John G. Torrey, Harvard University

Principles of Development and Differentiation

C. H. Waddington, University of Edinburgh

Additional Volumes in Preparation

Principles of Development and Differentiation

35

C. H. Waddington

University of Edinburgh

The Macmillan Company, New York

Collier-Macmillan Limited, London

Third Printing, 1967

Library of Congress catalog card number: 66-15030

The Macmillan Company, New York

Collier-Macmillan Canada, Ltd., Toronto, Ontario

PRINTED IN THE UNITED STATES OF AMERICA

Introduction

To ANYONE WITH HIS NORMAL QUOTA of curiosity, developing embryos are perhaps the most intriguing objects that nature has to show. If you look at one quite simply and straightforwardly, without any preconceptions, what you see—you can see it still better in a speeded-up motion-picture film, which makes things go more quickly—is a simple lump of jelly that, isolated in a drop of water or sitting on a dry surface, begins changing in shape and texture, developing new parts, sticking out processes, folding up some regions and spreading out in others, until it eventually turns into a recognizable small plant or worm or insect or some other type of organism. Nothing else that one can see puts on a performance which is both so apparently simple and spontaneous and yet, when you think about it, so mysterious.

One can watch a snow crystal growing on a windowpane; it produces elaborate patterns, but these are patterns depending on straight lines and definite angles and, therefore, obviously more simple than the definite but subtle shapes of animals. Again, one can watch a living cell which, of course, has a shape that is complex and not merely geometrical. A cell will eventually divide in two, and that is an impressive enough sight, but still all it is doing is to produce another cell like itself. The striking achievement of an egg is to produce things—roots, leaves, legs, eyes, backbones, and so on—which were not in it originally. It does more than merely reproduce itself; it produces something new. Even if you have a certain degree of biological knowledge when you start looking at it—knowing perhaps what everyone seems to know nowadays, that the fundamental characteristics of organisms are determined by the genes inherited from their parents, and that these genes are made of nucleic acid (DNA)—even so, merely to say that the lump of jelly you are looking at contains the right DNA to produce a rabbit leaves an enormous amount unaccounted for. Exactly how does the egg produce legs, head, eyes, intestine, and get up and start running about? Once you have seen the challenge that these phenomena offer to our understanding, the only hope of rescuing yourself from the seductions of embryology is to reflect that discretion may be the better part of valor, when you may conclude that development is really too difficult and you had better take up something simpler, such as biochemistry or genetics.

Embryology is, in fact, one of the main focal subjects within the whole wide area of biology. The attempt to discover the fundamental basis of living things by analyzing them into simpler and simpler elements has led, through the study of heredity and genetics, to the conclusion that ultimately the characteristics of any organism depend on its heredity—that is to say, on its genes; and, as most people know, we have by now a very good idea of the chemical constitution of those genes. They consist of DNA (which we shall discuss further in Chapter 2). But this is only the final analysis of the nature of living things. It is rather like saying that the engine of an automobile consists of electrons and protons. That is quite true, but it is by no means the whole story. The science that deals with the relation of the ultimate genes to the complex solid bodies of the living things we see around us is embryology, and it is this branch of biology that has the task of describing how the hereditary "determinants" actually do determine the production of various organs and characteristics of the final animal or plant.

Embryologists, therefore, have to study a whole series of types of biological organization which are more complex than the genes themselves. The chemistry of the genes, and the chemistry of the proteins they control, is only the very lowest level of organization with which we shall be concerned. We shall have to deal also with groups of genes; with various structures inside cells, such as the nucleus, membrane system, mitochondria, and the like; with whole cells; with tissues consisting of many cells, often of several different types; with organs, such as the brain or a limb made up of several tissues; and, finally, with the body as a whole. These are all different "levels of organization." Each higher level is dependent on the properties of a level below. They are not, of course, absolutely sharply divided from one another, but when we compare levels from different ends of the sequence—for instance, a limb with the organelles within a single cell—we are obviously dealing with two quite different types of entity. At first we shall have to tell rather different stories about them, but our ultimate aim must be to bring all the different theories together into a general synthesis that covers the whole range of levels. We are still a good long way from being able to do this.

The questions we shall discuss apply to plants as well as to animals, but, as we shall see, most of the problems are posed in a more acute form in the animal kingdom. Moreover, the development of animals has been more thoroughly studied. For both these reasons, animals will occupy the greater part of our discussion.

C. H. W.

Contents

1

The Problems of Development 1

The Basic Facts / Embryology and Evolution / The Meaning of Differentiation / The Integration of Development / The Development of Plants

2

Some Fundamental Problems 14

Preformation and Epigenesis / Embryology and Genetics / The Activities of Genes / Molecular Biology / The Molecular Biology of Embryos / Cell Biology

3

Histogenesis or Differentiation in Time 36

Genes and Proteins / The Development of Cells, Tissues, and Organs / The Canalization of Development / Is Differentiation Reversible? / Nuclear Transplantation

4

Regionalization and the Control of Gene Activity 59

The Control of Single Genes in Bacteria / The Control of Single Genes in Higher Organisms / The Control of Gene Sequences / Genetic Switch Mechanisms / The Amphibian Egg / The Early Chick Embryo / Physicochemical Nature of the Switch Mechanisms

5

Morphogenesis 90

Shapes of Single Cells / Small Group of Cells / Morphogenesis of Tissues / Multicellular Organs / The Final Stages / Concluding Remarks / Further Reading

Index 113

Principles of Development and Differentiation

CHAPTER 1

The Problems of Development

EMBRYOLOGY, LIKE ALL SCIENCES, begins with the observation of processes going on in nature, which it then tries to understand and explain. Before we can propose theories we need to know the problems they are intended to deal with. There are, of course, an enormous variety of different types of embryonic development in the animal world, corresponding to the great range of types of adult that are finally produced. However, one can get a good idea of the general problems we have to deal with by considering only one or two cases.

The Basic Facts

We will select two of the kinds of eggs that have been most studied experimentally—those of sea urchins and of newts. Figures 1·1 and 1·2 show a series of steps in the early development of these two types of eggs. Neither figure covers the whole of development. We shall not, in this book, discuss the preliminary processes of egg maturation in the ovary; and we shall take for granted the occurrence of meiotic divisions, by which the chromosome complement is reduced from the diploid to the haploid number, and of fertilization, by which the number is restored again. These are subjects for genetics rather than for embryology. The diagrams also do not illustrate development right up to the adult condition, but they trace it far enough to show the main kinds of process that occur during differentiation and thus to indicate the types of problem with which embryologists are faced.

It is obvious that there are certain similarities between the two

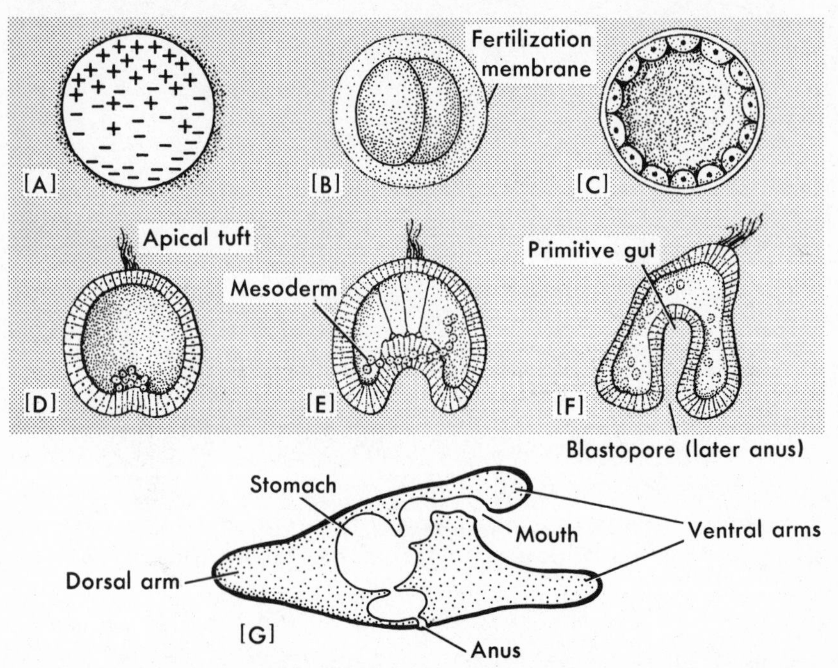

Figure 1·1. Early development of sea urchin. A: The fertilized egg as seen from the side. It floats with the animal pole upward and the vegetal pole downward. It is characterized by two gradients, one strongest at the animal pole falling off toward the vegetative pole, and the other running in the opposite direction. These are indicated by + for the first and by − for the second. **B:** The egg, after fertilization, has thrown off a membrane ("the fertilization membrane") and by this stage has divided into two. **C:** The egg is seen in vertical section. It has divided into a large number of cells which adhere to the fertilization membrane and leave a large hollow space in the center: this is the blastula stage. By the stage shown in **D** a group of cilia (the apical tuft) has appeared at the animal pole while the vegetative pole is beginning to become flattened and some cells are breaking free and moving into the interior of the blastula cavity. By the stage shown in **E** there are more of these cells, and some of them have put out processes that reach across the blastula cavity and attach to cells in the animal half of the egg. By the contraction of these attachment cells the vegetative end of the blastula is pulled gradually inward, forming a pocket which is the primitive gut. By the stage shown in **F** this has become a deep finger-shaped cavity reaching right across the blastula. Its top end is just beginning to be bent toward the right, which will become the ventral side of the larva. **G:** This end of the primitive gut has joined onto the ventral surface, and a hole has appeared at the point of junction: this is the mouth. Meanwhile, the four corners of the ventral side have been pulled out into arms and another pointed arm appears on the dorsal side, so that the whole larva has acquired the shape of a sharp pyramid lying on its side.

kinds of eggs. For instance, in both cases, in the first phase of development immediately after fertilization the original egg cell becomes divided into a larger number of small cells. This process, known as cleavage, takes place in eggs of all types. The processes at work are fundamentally those which are always concerned with cell division. They belong as much to the field of cell biology as to that of embryology, and we shall not discuss them in detail here, for lack of space.

At the end of the period of cleavage we see that the little embryo forms a collection of cells which is not a solid mass but is hollow in the center. This hollow sphere of cells is known as the blastula stage, and again it is one that can be found, in some form or other, in nearly all animal embryos. It is quite a transient stage and is immediately followed by a period characterized by a

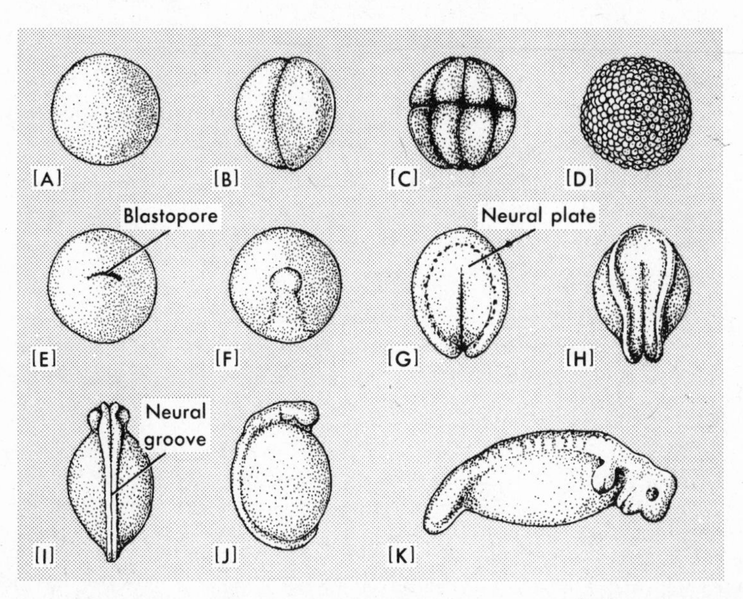

Figure 1·2. The development of an amphibian such as a newt or salamander. The egg first divides into a number of smaller cells and by the stage shown in **D** consists of a hollow ball of numerous cells. By the stage **E** the cells have become too small to be marked on the later drawings. In **E** the egg is seen from below (that is, from the vegetal pole). One can see a small crescent-shaped groove, the blastopore, which is actually the entrance into a narrow cavity that pushes into the interior of the hollow ball of cells. The crescent gradually grows round into a more circular shape (**F**). Shortly after this, if one looks at the egg from the opposite (animal) end (**G**), one can see a horseshoe-shaped area marked off on the surface by a ridge. This is the rudiment —the neural plate—from which the whole nervous system will develop. A little later (**H**) the boundary ridges (known as the "neural crest") have moved closer together. By the stage shown from on top in **I** and from the side in **J** the ridges have come together in the mid-dorsal lines, so that the whole neural area has been folded beneath the surface, where it forms a separate tube. The anterior end of this tube, toward the top in the diagrams, is already beginning to form the brain and nervous system of the head. By the stage shown in **K** the embryo is becoming elongated. In the head region, the eyes can be recognized, and somewhat behind this are two swellings, which are the rudiments of the gills. The tail is beginning to grow out at the posterior end.

number of foldings and movements of cell masses from one place to another. These foldings are known as the process of gastrulation, and again they occur, though in a variety of different ways, in the embryos of all classes of animals. They result in the production of

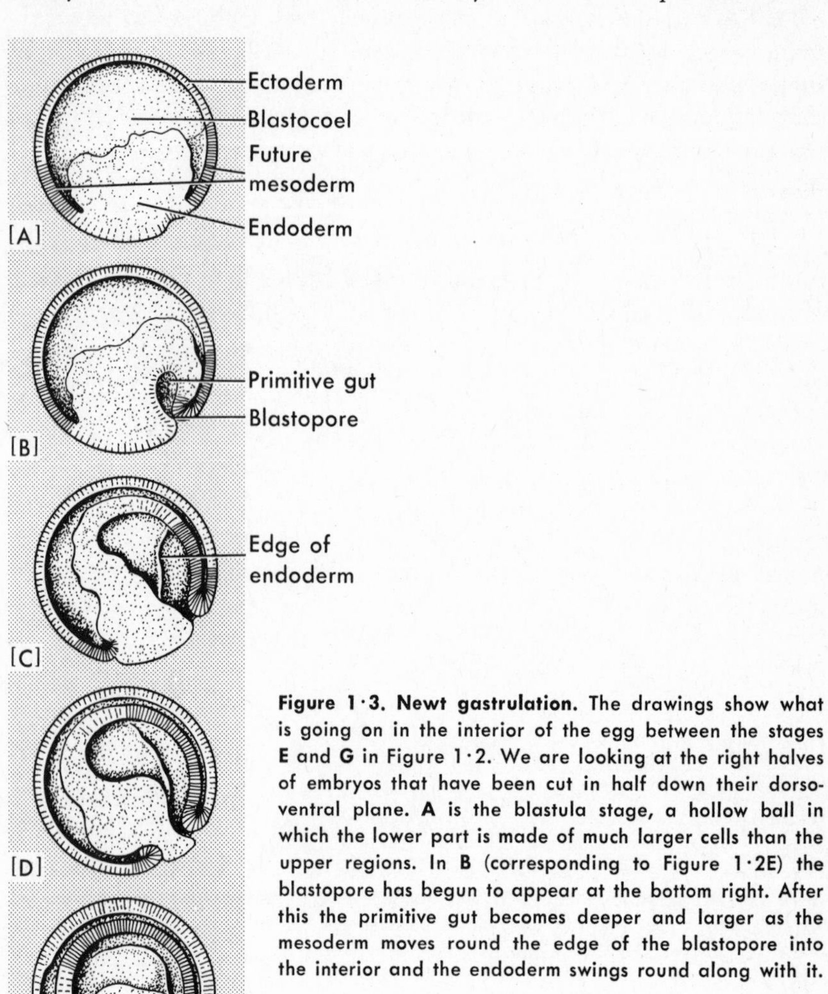

Figure 1·3. Newt gastrulation. The drawings show what is going on in the interior of the egg between the stages **E** and **G** in Figure 1·2. We are looking at the right halves of embryos that have been cut in half down their dorso-ventral plane. **A** is the blastula stage, a hollow ball in which the lower part is made of much larger cells than the upper regions. In **B** (corresponding to Figure 1·2E) the blastopore has begun to appear at the bottom right. After this the primitive gut becomes deeper and larger as the mesoderm moves round the edge of the blastopore into the interior and the endoderm swings round along with it.

an embryonic form that contains three layers. The outer layer forms the skin and the nervous system and is known as the ectoderm. The layer that lies deepest in the center of the embryo forms the intestine and its derivatives and is known as the endoderm. Between these two lies a middle layer, the mesoderm, which forms the muscles, skeleton, kidneys, and many other organs.

The processes by which these three layers are brought into being differ in different types of embryo (Figure 1·3), depending largely on the particular shape of the blastula from which the development starts. For instance, in the embryos of reptiles and birds the shape of the embryo is altered by the enormous supplies of nutritive material that have to be provided to keep the embryo alive within the egg shell until it is sufficiently developed to come out and feed for itself. The blastulae of these forms have been accommodated to the vast amount of yolk by becoming flat circular plates instead of hollow spherical balls (see Figure 4·10). Clearly the foldings necessary to produce three layers from a plate are quite different from those required to produce a similar set of layers from a hollow sphere. However, in both cases the end result of the foldings of gastrulation is the production of the three major layers—the ectoderm, mesoderm, and endoderm.

Once the three layers are formed they begin to develop into definite organs corresponding to those of the adult. For instance, in the sea urchin the endoderm soon begins to form a recognizable mouth, behind which is a stomach and an intestine leading to the anus. In the early stages of the embryo of the newt a very obvious and striking event is the formation of the nervous system. Part of the external ectoderm is first marked off from the rest by slightly elevated folds and is then folded inward to form a groove, and finally a tube, which gives rise to the brain and spinal cord and from which the rest of the nerves grow out. Meanwhile, the endoderm of the newt is also developing into the definitive regions of the intestine; and the mesoderm forms the first element of the skeleton, known as the notochord, along the center of the back, while on each side of it the tissue becomes divided up into a sequence of squarish blocks, the somites, which give rise to the muscles and bony skeleton of the backbone.

Embryology and Evolution

This book is mainly concerned with principles, and we shall not pursue further here a detailed discussion of the changes in anatomy which go on in various types of embryo. In the early history of embryology, up to about the end of the last century, these changes in morphology took the center of the stage. It was, of course, necessary for them to be described in detail first, before one could consider further how they were brought about. Even the mere description of them raised a number of apparently interesting problems. For instance, why is it that all embryos pass through a stage corresponding to the blastula, and then through a process of gastrulation to reach a three-layered condition? There was no apparent answer until Darwin's theory of evolution became accepted about the middle of the last century. Then it seemed clear that this similarity in the embryos of different forms must be related in some way to the fact that animals are evolved one from the other. Even before this time von Baer had formulated one general "law" about such morphological comparisons between embryos, stating that the more general features of an animal, which are common to all members of a large group, appear earlier during embryonic development than the specialized features that characterize any particular species. With the coming of evolution theory this idea was reformulated by Haeckel into the rule that the stages in the embryonic development of an animal in some way repeat the stages of the evolution of its ancestors. The main reason for mentioning these old ideas here is that this "law" has become very widely known, and is often repeated in the phrase that during its development an animal "climbs up its family tree."

This is a memorable and catchy expression, but it is actually quite misleading. The embryonic stages of any highly evolved animal are never at all closely similar to the adult stages of its ancestors. They do, however, sometimes look like embryonic stages of the evolutionary ancestors. For instance, it is generally accepted that the mammals, including man, evolved from fishlike forms. These ancestral fish had gills provided with gill slits through which the water could circulate. Human embryos at a certain stage have slits in the same position as gill slits. However, they do not look like the gill slits of adult fish, though they have some resemblance to the gill slits of embryonic fish. But there is nothing very profound in this, it is just what we would have expected. If a fish or any other type of animal is to change during evolution, it is almost inevitable that these changes will take place gradually, by slight modifications of the existing pattern of organization. Now, if an early embryonic stage is changed, for instance, by a gene mutation, this will probably cause alterations in many subsequent stages, and it is only to be expected that the final result on the adult will be considerable, and therefore almost certainly harmful and most unlikely to survive the rigors of natural selection. The changes that will be preserved to form part of the evolutionary sequence are most likely to be relatively small ones occurring in the later stages of development when they do not have such drastic consequences. Thus we should expect that most of the changes involved in the evolution from fish to man will have affected relatively late stages of embryonic development, so that the early stages, when the gill slits first appear, are likely to remain almost unaltered throughout the whole evolutionary process; and this is just what we find.

It is, moreover, quite inappropriate to try to use evolutionary arguments to provide a causal explanation of embryo development, as some of the early evolutionists did. It is not at all sufficient, to our present way of thinking, to say that a human embryo possesses gill slits because it was evolved from a fish which also possesses gill slits. This is true enough as far as it goes, but we want to be able to go much further and to state what processes and reactions going on within this particular egg, which we see in front of us, cause it to develop the structures that we see appearing. We want to understand the immediate causes, as well as the historical derivation, of the changes that we see proceeding in any given instance of embryonic development.

The Meaning of Differentiation

The rest of this book will be concerned with trying to discover at least the general nature of these causal processes. Before starting on this task it is necessary to emphasize again something of the complexity of the problems that have to be solved. Perhaps the best way to clarify the issues is to distinguish three *types* of process that we shall have to deal with. They are often lumped together under the name "differentiation," but one can distinguish three major categories of change: differentiation in time, differentiation in space, and differentiation in shape.

DIFFERENTIATION IN TIME

If one watches any particular small region of an egg it will be found gradually to change in character as time goes on. First it is a part of the general substance of the egg. As the egg undergoes cleavage into many cells the region will become provided with its own nuclei and cell membranes and become a mass of cells, but at first these cells are of a very general kind. A little later the cells will begin to form some particular tissue of the adult—for instance, part of a muscle, of a bone, of a kidney, and so on. In doing so, the cells must change in chemical composition; a muscle cell must develop the contractile proteins of the muscle fibers, and bone cell must lay down the bone substances, and so on. There is, therefore, a sequence of changes as time passes, by which this region of the egg gradually acquires the characteristics of some specialized tissue of the adult. Since this process results in the production of an adult tissue, it is technically referred to as *histogenesis.*

DIFFERENTIATION IN SPACE

The egg, at the time of fertilization, is more or less similar (though never exactly the same) in all its parts. It is still usually pretty uniform when it is divided into a number of cells and becomes a blastula. Gradually, however, one part of it will become a brain, another part an intestine, and each of these will become subdivided again into a forebrain, midbrain, hindbrain, and so on; into the esophagus, stomach, gut, and the rest of it. There is an obvious production of many more different regions of the embryo than there were to start with. As a matter of fact, as we shall see, eggs at the time of fertilization are not entirely uniform throughout their whole mass. They always start with some regional differences between one part and another, but at first there are very few differences and these are usually slight and difficult to detect. Later there are many more regional differences, and they are more striking and well marked. The process by which the egg becomes divided into many distinct different regions is known as *regionalization.*

DIFFERENTIATION IN SHAPE

Eggs usually have a very simple shape, often spherical. The organisms into which they develop have, of course, complicated shapes. Not only is their overall external surface molded into a structure of trunk, legs, head, tail, and what have you, but internally they contain many different organs, each with a rather constant and particular shape. The processes by which these changes in shape occur are known as *morphogenesis.*

The Integration of Development

In any ordinary embryo all these three processes—of histogenesis, regionalization, and morphogenesis—are going on simultaneously and in intimate connection with one another. The reason for separating them is that it is clear that they call for different types of explanation. Histogenesis, for instance, is a change in the nature of the substance in a particular region; that is to say, it could be explained in purely chemical terms. Regionalization is also a chemical process, involving the production of different substances in different regions of the embryo. Again it demands a chemical explanation, but one that can show how different chemical processes will occur in the different places that become regionally distinct. Morphogenesis is quite different. It involves masses of material becoming changed in shape; that is to say, it demands an explanation in terms of processes that will give rise to forces, which can push the material out of its original shape into another. These processes, of course, are certain to involve chemical reactions, but the causes of the morphogenesis will not be the chemical reactions themselves but the forces to which they give rise.

It is important to remember that all these three types of process can go on both at the cell level and at the tissue level. For instance, when a cell of the early mesoderm gradually changes into a muscle cell we have histogenesis at the cell level. In many cases, however, it does not seem to be possible to persuade single cells to undergo certain types of histogenesis. They only do so when forming part of a larger group of cells, and in that case we have histogenesis at the tissue level. Similarly the example of regionalization quoted —that is, the division of the nervous system into later parts of the brain and the spinal cord—is at the tissue level; but we can find it at the cell level also, for instance, in the formation of the central body, dendrites, and axon of a single nerve cell. Again we quoted examples of morphogenesis at the tissue level, but we can find single cells or groups of very small numbers of cells in which morphogenesis and the formation of a definite shape also occur. Thus we have to look for explanations of processes of different kinds taking place at different levels of biological organization.

The Development of Plants

Fundamentally plants resemble animals in that they also begin life as a single fertilized egg cell. The processes by which this cell is converted into the fully formed plant differ in certain respects from those that occur in animal embryos. Put in its simplest terms, one may say that in the plant a well-defined and limited embryonic phase is not a characteristic of development, but that in a sense differentiation continues throughout the life of the plant and is therefore normally accompanied by growth.

The egg cell of the higher plant is enclosed in an embryo sac which is surrounded by a nutritive tissue, the nucellus. The embryo sac also contains an endosperm nucleus which combines with a male gamete at the time of fertilization. After fertilization the egg cell develops into an embryo and the endosperm nucleus into a tissue, the endosperm, to which the nutritive materials of the nucellus are transferred. The growth of the embryo depends on the nutrients released from the endosperm. Thus the position with respect to the early development of the embryo in the higher plant is different from that in the animal, where the nutritive reserve is within the egg cell in the form of yolk. The early plant embryo is in the form of a spherical group of cells. From this, in essence, an axis is generated with a growth region, or meristem, at each end.

The meristems have a peculiar and decisive significance, since it is due to them that embryonic activity and differentiation are continued into the adult phase of the plant. Further, through them much of the growth of the plant is maintained, and they therefore display the intimate relationship between growth and differentiation that is characteristic of plants. They consist of small isodiametric cells which have a large nucleus, are nonvacuolated, and have a thin wall which consists almost entirely of pectin. Division is relatively rapid in the meristems and they yield cells that become the basis for the construction of the organs of the root and the shoot.

The root presents the simpler situation and may be considered first. Division is continuous in the meristem, and new cells are continuously being added to the root, which increases the size of the organ while maintaining it as a cylindrical structure. The cells that are contributed to the axis are at first apparently all more or less similar to each other and to the meristematic cells from which they are formed. Immediately, however, many of them become involved in a process of expansion in the course of which various types of cells differentiate. During expansion there may be a hundredfold increase in the volume of the cell. This is due largely to the development of a central vacuole with a consequent accumulation of water. It is accompanied by a considerable growth of the wall and to a lesser extent of the cytoplasm and nucleus. The differentiation of the different types of cells during expansion may involve the assumption of different shapes through particular patterns of growth in the wall and the assumption of different metabolic patterns through changes in the constitution of the cytoplasm.

From some of the cells arising from the apical meristem in some plants further meristems may be formed. These secondary meristems arise from cells that are relatively large and vacuolated. In particular positions some of these vacuolated cells start dividing and may ultimately yield two meristems, which in due course become in effect two concentric cylinders of meristematic cells. The inner of these is known as the cambium and gives rise to cells that become differentiated into conducting elements, while the outer, the phellogen, gives rise to cork on its outer surface and general root tissue on its inner. At the stage when the cambium is being formed, cells just outside the conducting elements may proliferate to form a new apical meristem, which then grows out forming the tip of a branch, and this gives rise to a whole new cycle of growth and development.

In the shoot, development is somewhat more complicated but depends on the same basic process of the growth of meristematic regions that give rise to cells that become differentiated during expansion. The apical shoot meristem has a greater tendency than that of the root to become divided into separate growth centers, and these in turn become differentiated to give the initiating centers ("initials") of leaves and buds on the sides of the elongating shoot. At a later stage the apical shoot meristem may also change its character and start to produce the initials of reproductive organs such as flowers, instead of vegetative organs such as leaves. The apical meristem of the shoot gives rise to cells that may ultimately become incorporated into a cylindrical meristem, the cambium, which produces cells that become differentiated into elements of the conducting tissue. External to this cylinder another may be formed from vacuolated cells which divide to give externally protective corky layers. Once again the processes of cell differentiation are usually accompanied by considerable cell expansion. Visible signs of differentiation may be seen in the formation of intracellular inclusions, such as chloroplasts and pigment granules, and are often strongly expressed in the formation of nonliving cellulose structures on the cell walls (for example, in the various types of cell making up wood, bark, cork). However, although there are undoubtedly differences in the metabolic activity of the cytoplasms of different types of plant cell, we rarely see in them the formation of such markedly different internal cytoplasms as those characteristic of animal tissues, such as muscle, liver, nerve, pancreas, and intestinal epithelium.

Clearly the pattern of differentiation for the organism as a whole is very materially different in a plant and an animal. Differentiation in the two systems differs in another important respect. The organs and tissues of a plant are markedly labile. When a mature organ has been produced it carries the capacity to produce another organ or even a whole plant vegetatively. Roots are readily produced from mature stems, and buds may be produced from the margins of leaves and from the cut surfaces of roots. Vegetative buds may even be produced in flowers. The only living parts of the plant whose activity cannot apparently be modified materially are the terminal meristems. The apical meristem of the shoot cannot be induced to grow into a root, or that of the root into a shoot or a flower.

The generally labile character of the living tissues of mature plant organs is perhaps most vividly shown by the phenomenon of callus formation. When *mature* tissue is removed aseptically from an organ and transferred to a suitable sterile medium, random proliferation occurs and an irregular mass of tissue is formed. In due course meristems are formed in this callus, and these may develop into roots, shoots, or even flowers. The evidence suggests that all living normal mature tissues of the plant will produce a callus, and that from any callus any organ or a whole plant may be produced. Clearly every single living cell of the plant is totipotent and carries the capacity to produce a whole plant. This has recently been demonstrated in a particularly dramatic form by work which has shown that a whole plant can be generated from a single cell from a callus culture.

This tissue reversibility is, of course, shown only by living cells of the plant. The dead tissues of wood and cork cannot and do not display the phenomenon. However, these inert cells constitute only a relatively small proportion (about 5 per cent) of the cellular population of an annual herbaceous plant. When a change in the differentiation state occurs, cell division is always involved. As a result of this, new walls are laid down within the confines of those of the mature cell, and the daughter cells are inevitably reduced in size. At the same time the metabolic state of the cell changes, and the central vacuole may be diminished.

Differentiation in the plant may not lead to the formation of cells with such totally different constituents as we find in the muscle, nerve, digestive, and gland cells of animals. Moreover, as we have shown, it occurs by quite different processes. At the same time it is evident that plants undergo the three types of differentiation described earlier: differentiation in time, as a cell changes from a meristematic condition to one of the types characteristic of the various tissues of the root, leaf, or stem; in space, when the original embryo gives rise to a shoot apex and a root apex; and in shape, when the initials of leaves and flowers grow out into structures of characteristic form, or individual cells lay down the cellulose exoskeletons characteristic of various types of tissue.

Owing to their great plasticity and the comparative poverty of their internal cytoplasmic differentiation, plant cells do not pose the problems of development in quite such a forceful form as we encounter it in animal embryos. Most of the further discussion in this book will therefore be focused on the development of animals.

CHAPTER

2

Some Fundamental Problems

THE STUDY OF DEVELOPMENT has a very long history. It has fascinated thinkers and observers ever since the time of the ancient Greeks. Of course, the greater part of what writers of earlier centuries had to say has since been superseded. Even their descriptions of what they saw are, in these days of electron microscopes and other instruments, quite inadequate. Most of their detailed ideas seem to us now mainly of historical interest, particularly after the great "leap forward" brought about by the rise of molecular biology, which many people see as a revolutionary advance as drastic as the step by which a pupa turns into a butterfly. But an embryologist will never forget that a butterfly still contains many organs that it took over from the larva and pupa from which it developed. Our present ideas about embryology are inevitably greatly influenced by the history of that science. The work of the biologists in past centuries laid the foundations on which we have to build, and it is worth having a short glance at it to discover the points of lasting value it contains.

Preformation and Epigenesis

Right at the beginning of the history of embryology in the fourth century B.C., Aristotle formulated a major problem that has haunted the subject ever since. He distinguished between two ideas, which have become known as "preformation" and "epigenesis." Preformation is the notion that the egg at the time of fertilization already contains something corresponding to every feature that will eventually be present in the fully formed adult. Certain eighteenth-century anatomists, shortly after the microscope was invented, thought in fact that they could see a complete little man located in the head of the sperm, or a shadowy figure of the final animal embedded in the egg. This was, of course, mere imagination, dependent on the inadequacy of their instruments. However, the basic idea of preformation is not that every feature of the adult is already present as such in the fertilized egg; it is rather that in the egg every feature is represented by *something,* though this may be quite different from the adult form of the feature. The idea complementary to this is epigenesis, which supposes that many features of the adult are not represented at all in the fertilized egg, which contains only a smaller number of elements, and that during development these react together to produce the much larger number of adult features.

A discussion of the merits of these opposing views was carried on vigorously for many centuries. Nowadays, the issue *ought* to be finally settled and understood. We know that a fertilized egg contains *some* preformed elements—namely, the genes and a certain number of different regions of cytoplasm—and we know that during development these interact in epigenetic processes to produce final adult characters and features that are not individually represented in the egg. We see, therefore, that both preformation and epigenesis are involved in embryonic development.

In the present stage of biology, the study of the preformed element in the fertilized eggs, taken in hand by the geneticists, has made such enormous progress that nobody is likely to be able to overlook it for long. Embryologists certainly have to accept it as part of the basic groundwork from which they start. Their attention is more immediately concentrated on trying to understand the causal processes by which the genes interact with one another and with the cytoplasm of the egg. The focus of their interest is in the processes that we have referred to as epigenesis. In fact, the word "epigenetics" is a quite appropriate name for the whole causal study of development, emphasizing, as it does, its fundamental dependence on genetics and its interest in causes and processes.

Embryology and Genetics

The beginnings of a causal analysis of development were made toward the end of the last century and the early part of this one, at a time when genetics was only just starting to become a science. The people who first concerned themselves with the experimental analysis of embryonic processes did not realize the basic importance of genetics to their system of ideas. They did not refer to themselves as epigeneticists, but called their science by the rather clumsy titles of "developmental mechanics" or "developmental physiology." The ideas they used were not taken from any other organized part of biological thought, such as genetics, but were "operational" concepts, defined in relation to particular types of experiment. They were appropriate for describing the results of the experiments but not really capable of explaining them in terms of any other system of ideas. This is the way in which most sciences have to start, since at the beginning of the development of a science there is no already-existing system of ideas in terms of which explanations can be made.

Later in the book we shall have to describe some of these experiments, since many of them have revealed the processes that are still the major puzzles we have to understand. We shall then also have to discuss in rather more detail the early theoretical concepts—such as the distinction between "regulation eggs," which can produce a normal adult even after injury, as opposed to "mosaic eggs," in which each part from the beginning is fixed in the way it is going to develop; or the idea of "induction," which supposes that one part of the egg "induces" its neighboring parts to develop in conformity with itself; or the idea of an "embryonic field" as a region throughout the whole of which there is some influence that causes the appearance of an organized complete entity such as a limb. Here all that is necessary is to point out that these concepts and many like them contain no obvious reference to genetics or the hereditary constitution.

This is not to say, of course, that the role of heredity was completely unappreciated. Perhaps the greatest of the early experimental embryologists was the German, Boveri. One of his major interests, among many others, was the role of the nucleus during development, and he realized that the nucleus was probably the bearer of hereditary determinants. He was able to make many fundamental contributions to our understanding of hereditary processes. For instance, he was the first person to demonstrate clearly that chromosomes differ in their properties in controlling development. Again he showed that the epigenetic processes of development frequently involve an interaction between the nucleus and the particular type of cytoplasm surrounding it (Figure 2·1). This is an absolutely basic fact and is still one that we are struggling to understand more thoroughly (see Chapter 4).

In Boveri's time little more was known about genetics than the basic laws of Mendel. It was not till after the geneticists had worked out a more comprehensive chromosome theory of heredity that they began to have many valuable insights to offer to the embryologists. Since one of the main themes of this book is that embryology has to base itself on a solid foundation of genetics, it is worth looking a little more closely at the history of the intrusion of genetic ideas into embryological thinking. It has been a very

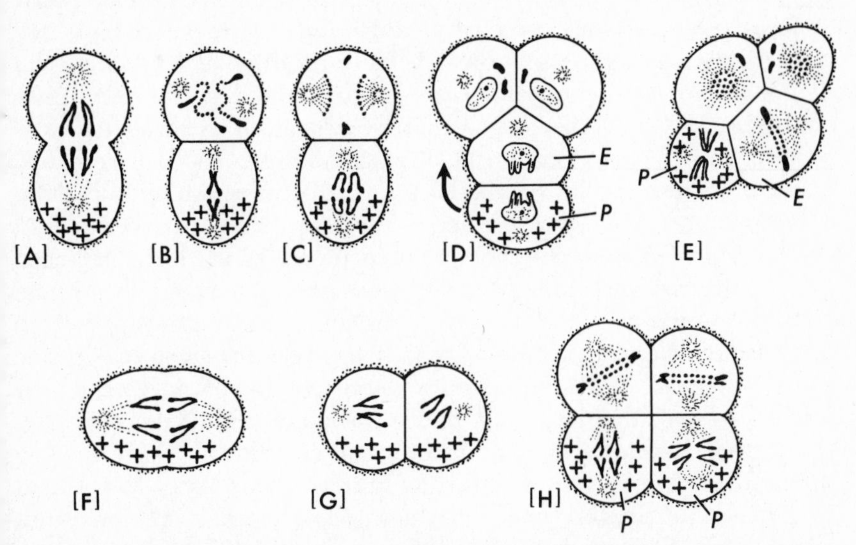

Figure 2·1. First cleavages of the egg of Ascaris (a threadworm parasite in the gut of the horse). The upper row shows the normal cleavages. The organism has only two chromosomes, and these are distributed equally to the two daughter cells (**A**). In the second division (**B** and **C**) the chromosomes in the upper animal cell become broken down into a large number of fragments, and the tips of the chromosomes do not move to the ends of the spindle and are not included in the two new nuclei. After the division the most vegetative cell (labeled *P*) moves round in the direction of the arrow (**D**). When the next division begins (**E**), the chromosomes in the cell labeled *E* have also fragmented, and it is only those in cell *P* that remain complete. After centrifuging the egg, the cleavage is sometimes abnormal in the way shown in the lower row. At the second division fragmention takes place in both the upper cells but in neither of the lower cells, both of which act like *P* cells. This was interpreted by Boveri as evidence for the existence, at the vegetative end of the egg, of a special cytoplasmic substance whose distribution is indicated by the crosses in the diagram.

gradual process, and has still far to go in orthodox embryological circles. For instance, most authoritative general texts on embryology include very little about genetics.

Actually, it was the man who made the breakthrough into modern genetics who also made the first major contribution of genetic thought to embryological problems. The chromosome theory of heredity was elaborated by T. H. Morgan and his school (Bridges,

Sturtevant, and Muller) at Columbia University in the couple of decades after 1910. Morgan had begun his scientific life as an embryologist, and toward the end of his life he more or less gave up genetics and returned to his first love—embryos are about the most seductive objects in nature to the mind capable of wonder and curiosity. Even in the intermediate period, when so much of his attention must have been taken up with the great breakthrough of Drosophila genetics, as exciting in its time as molecular biology is today, he found time to write a book on *Embryology and Genetics* (1934). He firmly advocated the point—and should have fully established it, if people had been ready to listen to him—that the fundamental agents that bring about embryonic development are the genes, and the only finally satisfactory theory of embryology must be a theory of how the activities of genes are controlled.

This is a very general though basic point. If we look for more particular principles that Morgan established, the most important is this. As we have said, Boveri had demonstrated that embryonic development depends on the interaction of the nucleus (containing genes, of course) with the different regions of cytoplasm with which the egg is provided. Morgan made the point that the pattern in which the regions of cytoplasm are arranged in the egg, and thus the pattern of the embryo into which it develops, is itself determined by genes—namely, the genes that operate in the cells of the maternal ovary while the egg is being matured. This is a basic point for biology. A few decades ago many biologists who had not appreciated this point argued that genes control the final finicky details of organisms, say, the color of their eyes or hair or flowers or the precise molecular architecture of the hemoglobin in their blood cells, but that the basic pattern of the organism—that it has a head in front and a backbone down the back and four legs, one at each corner—is not a matter for genetics. They argued that it cannot be investigated by crossing animals of radically different overall pattern—a bilaterally symmetrical vertebrate with a pentagonally symmetrical echinoderm for instance—and that, therefore, geneticists cannot prove that their much-vaunted genes are able to produce anything more than superficial embellishments added to a basic structure which is determined in some quite different way.

If this were true it would be a point of overriding importance. It would imply, for instance, that genetics might be important when we are considering the evolution of two species that are quite like one another—for instance, house flies and mosquitos, both of which have six legs and two wings—but that genetics would be quite unable to throw any light on the evolutionary relationships between types of animals that are radically different in pattern—for instance, insects which have six legs and spiders which have eight. It is, therefore, worth looking in a little more detail at the evidence against it.

It is true that there are comparatively few cases in which you can make crosses between individuals that differ in the fundamental basic pattern and thus make a classical genetic analysis of the differences. However, there are a few instances in which this is possible. One of them, with which Morgan and his group were concerned, is the fresh water snail, *Limnaea peregra.* This little creature forms a shell twisted into a spiky spire. It exists in two races. In the common one the spiral runs in the direction conventionally called right-handed—the same direction as a normal wood screw. In the other race it runs in the opposite direction. Anyone who has ever met a left-handed screw and finally discovered, after losing his temper, that his efforts to undo it were only forcing it in tighter and tighter will realize that these two forms of screw are basically different in pattern. One is, in fact, the mirror image of the other, and there is no way within the limits of three-dimensional space in which a right-handed screw can be turned round, put upside down, stood on its head, or twisted about in any other way that will convert it into a left-handed screw. The two forms are different and distinct patterns, but the animals inhabiting the shells are similar enough to be crossed and produce hybrid offspring.

When this experiment was done, the inheritance of right- or left-handedness at first glance seemed very peculiar. It was one of Morgan's group, Sturtevant, who pointed out that the situation is really quite simple. Handedness is inherited as a simple Mendelian gene, with right-handed dominant to left-handed. The only oddity in the situation is that the handedness of any particular shell depends, not on the genes that the snail inhabiting the shell contains, but on the genes that were in the maternal ovary in which the egg was matured. The right-handedness or left-handedness of a snail is not a character that develops late in life; it is a property of the egg cell itself, and can be recognized as soon as the egg has divided into four cells (Figure 2·2). In fact, quite recently it has been shown that it can be recognized even earlier. While the egg cell of Limnaea is growing up to its full size in the maternal ovary it is surrounded by follicle cells through which the yolk and other necessary materials for the developing egg are pumped into it. These follicle cells leave a trace of themselves on the surface of the egg in the form of spots which can be stained with certain dyes. They are arranged in an asymmetrical way. It is not yet certain that this

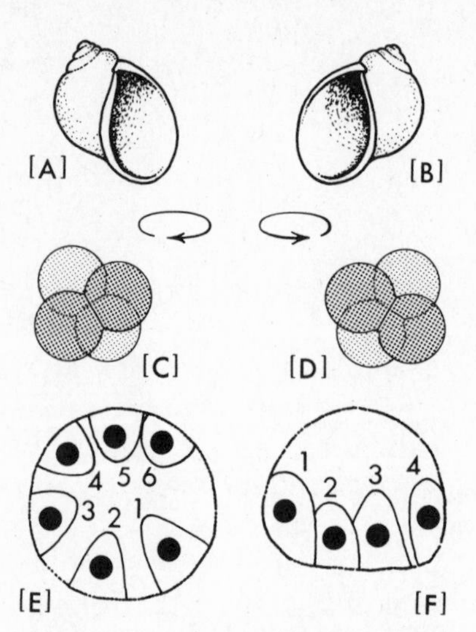

Figure 2·2. Limnea. A and B show, respectively, the right-handed and the left-handed form of the spiral snail shell. C and D show the corresponding stages of the egg. E and F show the egg cell during its maturation in the ovary, when it is clothed with six follicle cells asymmetrically arranged.

asymmetry of the spots is reversed in the left-handed and right-handed eggs. It is clear, however, that the genes in the mother could control the arrangement of the follicle cells, and determine in this way the asymmetry which becomes visible during the cleavage of the egg. In any case, the basic pattern of the individual snail is, after all, totally dependent on genes—but on the genes of the mother, not on the genes in the individual itself.

This point is so important for the whole theory, not only of embryology but of evolution, that it is worth quoting another case. In all flies, including the fruit fly Drosophila on which so much genetics has been done, the body of the adult consists of a head, behind which is a thorax made up of three major segments, known as the prothorax, the mesothorax, and the metathorax. Each thoracic segment bears a pair of legs, while the mesothorax also carries a pair of wings, and the metathorax a pair of small appendages known as halters or balancers, which function as a gyroscopic organ by which the animal keeps itself flying upright; behind the thorax is an abdomen with which we need not now be concerned. Flies belong to the class Diptera—that is to say, insects with two wings—whereas most insects, such as butterflies, have four wings, one pair derived from the mesothorax and one pair derived from the metathorax. From the point of view of evolution the difference between a dipteran and a normal insect is, by any reckoning, a change in the basic pattern of the organism.

How far are we entitled to say that it is controlled by genes? The answer is, very completely. In the first place, we know quite a number of genes in Drosophila—the so-called bithorax series—

that make wings grow out of the metathoracic segment of the animal that contains them. This fact is one major step toward understanding the evolution of new animal patterns. A single gene can change a dipteran into the normal type of insect with four wings.

There is a further point that is important for the theories both of evolution and of embryology. One does not expect natural selection often to accept, as adequately efficient, a gene that suddenly produces a major change in the character of an organism; in fact, drosophilas in which the bithorax genes produce an extra wing are usually very feeble individuals which would hardly be expected to survive under natural circumstances. It is, therefore, important to know that besides single genes that can produce this pattern at one blow, as it were, there are a whole series of mildly and, from a natural selective point of view, inoffensively operating genes, which have a tendency to operate in this direction, so that when enough of them have been brought together by selection the switch from two wings to four wings suddenly occurs. That is looking at the question from the point of view of evolution. From the standpoint of embryology, it is equally important to realize that a major switch in the developmental program (from "a group of cells in the metathoracic rudiment produce a halter" to "the same group of cells in the metathorax produce a wing") can be brought about not only by one gene, which presumably produces just one protein or enzyme, but equally well by the activities of a whole

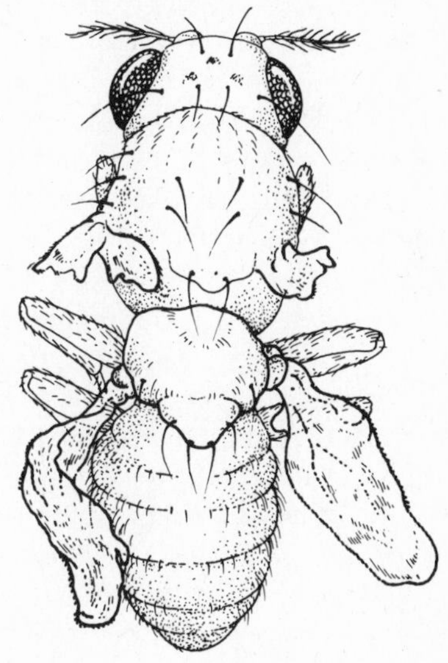

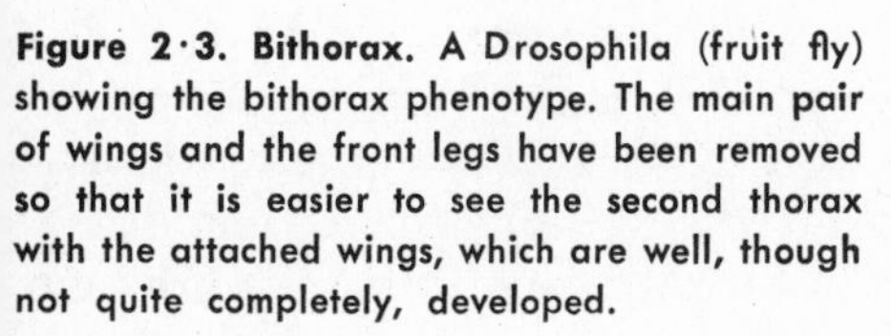

Figure 2·3. Bithorax. A Drosophila (fruit fly) showing the bithorax phenotype. The main pair of wings and the front legs have been removed so that it is easier to see the second thorax with the attached wings, which are well, though not quite completely, developed.

group of genes, each of which must be producing a different protein or enzyme. We shall return to this question when considering the nature of embryological switch mechanisms (page 69).

The point to be made here is that Morgan was absolutely justified in arguing that every aspect—even the most general—of biological form is ultimately under the control of genes (or genelike bodies—see page 35) and that there is no serious case for arguing that organisms have a basic nongenetic pattern to which the genes of the geneticists just add a few superficial ornaments, as regrettably "architects" have sometimes been persuaded to plaster a little Renaissance detail onto the façade of buildings put up by competent engineers. Genes are engineers as well as architects, though they may take an extra generation to convert a railway station into a heliport!

The Activities of Genes

During the hectic period in the 1920's and 1930's when the modern chromosomal theory of heredity was being built up, few embryologists, other than Morgan himself, were interested in genetics, and few geneticists in embryology. It was only in the later part of this period that the two subjects began to come together again. The approaches to their common ground were made from two different directions. A few embryologists began to ask themselves how the development of a particular embryonic organ is modified and controlled by genetic factors. I had better confess, since it may color the presentation I shall give in this book, that this has always been the question by which I have been particularly fascinated.

It is obvious that the development of tissues and organs in highly evolved multicellular organisms is influenced by many genes, not just by one or two. The problems we face are concerned with the activities of large groups of genes. The most important general conclusion that has emerged is that the genes in such groups are not independent in their activity but interact with one another in such a way as to give rise to a limited number of rather definite types of developmental change, which convert the initial general embryonic cells into a certain number of specific kinds of adult cells and tissues—liver cells, nerve cells, muscle cells, and so on. This type of interaction, which is known as "canalization," will be discussed more fully in Chapter 3.

Most geneticists interested in development asked themselves a rather different question: how does any particular gene produce its effects? The most important early worker along these lines was the German-American biologist Richard Goldschmidt. He performed a very important service in directing people's attention to this matter, but his basic idea was only partially correct. He supposed that genes act always by controlling the *rate* at which a given reaction goes on. This is in a way true as far as it goes, but Goldschmidt did not see the point that genes control the rates of reactions not only, as he suspected, by influencing the quantity of enzymes produced, but also, and even more importantly by changing the chemical constitution of the enzymes so as to alter their efficiency. This point began to emerge in studies made in England on the development of flower pigments and, particularly, in the work of an American-French team (G. W. Beadle and Boris Ephrussi) on the genetic control of the eye colors in Drosophila.

Workers on these subjects soon realized that the pigments in flower petals and insect eyes are not directly produced by the genes, but are manufactured by the aid of enzymes, and that the prime activity of the genes is on the nature of these enzymes. Beadle and his collaborator Tatum worked out a way in which it is possible to study these enzymes rather directly. They used a lowly organism, the fungus Neurospora, which can normally manufacture all the substances required for its life (except one or two vitamins) out of very simple raw materials such as sugars and inorganic salts, including nitrates. Geneticists had by this time discovered how to induce gene changes or mutations by the action of x-rays. It was found that some of the mutant types induced in Neurospora had lost the ability to synthesize some particular relatively complex compound out of these simple basic materials. The mutation had, in fact, caused the disappearance of the activity of the enzyme concerned with this particular synthesis. On this basis Beadle erected one of the great generalizations of physiological genetics, the so-called one-gene-one-enzyme hypothesis. This states that each gene is concerned with the production in the cell of one particular enzyme. As we shall see later, there may be genes that are doing something else (for example, controlling the activities of other genes) and for which this generalization is not true. However, it is certainly true of a great many genes, and these are nowadays referred to as "structural genes" because they control the chemical structure of an enzyme molecule.

The formulation of this hypothesis in the early 1940's marked the beginning of the modern period of developmental studies. It ushered in a period of enormously rapid development both of ideas and of methods and techniques of investigation. Within a few years genetics took on a new look. It had been founded on experiments of breeding and hybridizing animals such as rabbits and fruit flies. It started now to deal with organisms such as bacteria and viruses, where enormously greater numbers can be handled and thus greater precision obtained. The old experimental methods, dependent mainly on breeding, were supplemented with a whole range of new techniques—the use of the electron microscope, the ultracentrifuge, x-ray crystallography, paper chromatography, and so on. It was a real breakthrough on many fronts. It led to the development of a body of knowledge and ideas that is usually referred to as "molecular biology." It is impossible in a book devoted to the principles of development to summarize the whole of this massive advance in fundamental biology. However, some of its ideas are absolutely essential to our present outlook on all biological problems. We will, therefore, give in the next section a short and necessarily superficial summary, in unduly dogmatic terms, from which many of the complexities have been omitted, of those molecular biological ideas that seem to be most important for our understanding of embryonic development.

Molecular Biology

The focus of the new developments is an understanding of the nature of the genetic material. We have known for a long time that this material lies in the chromosomes. In higher organisms the chromosomes consist of a combination of nucleic acids and proteins. Until about twenty years ago we had little idea how either of these classes of compound are constituted in detail. Since then we have learned that both are in the form of long linear sequences of relatively small building blocks. In the proteins these building blocks are amino acids; in nucleic acids, they are nucleotide bases combined with sugar and phosphate to make nucleosides. The critical point came with the demonstration that one of these two classes of compound is the paramount one and the real bearer of the hereditary constitution. In microorganisms such as bacteria and viruses there are no true chromosomes containing both protein and nucleic acid. It was found, first by Avery and McLeod, that nucleic acid extracted from one strain of bacteria will sometimes enter the cells of another strain, and can then confer on this second strain some hereditary qualities derived from the first. This process of "transformation" clearly shows that it is nucleic acid that is the bearer of hereditary information.

Once this point began to emerge it was easy to suggest that the sequence of the unit nucleotides in the nucleic acid could determine the sequence of amino acids in corresponding proteins. These might be not only the proteins of the chromosomes themselves, but also the proteins that are formed in the rest of the cell and act as enzymes in cellular metabolism. This suggestion was strongly reinforced as new methods of x-ray crystallography and chemical analysis began to throw light on the precise structure of the nucleic acids and proteins. The work of Watson, Crick, and Wilkins led to a picture of the chromosomal nucleic acid as a "double helix," consisting of two threads twisted round one another like the strands of a rope. The two threads are composed of unit building blocks, each of which contains one out of a set of four nucleotides—known as thymine, adenine, guanine, and cytosine. Each building block also contains a phosphate group and, in the type of nucleic acid found in most chromosomes (known as DNA), a molecule of the sugar deoxyribose. There is no restriction on the order in which the nucleotides can be strung together in any one thread. We may have a sequence ATTGCT or any other sequence one pleases.

Normally the two strings adhere together in pairs twisted round each other to form a helix with a screwlike configuration. There is a very stringent limitation on the sequences that can pair together in this way. When adenine is present at a given place in one sequence, thymine must be present in the corresponding place in the complementary strand, and similarly guanine must go with cytosine. Thus when the sequence in one strand is fixed, the sequence in the corresponding strand is automatically determined also.

This fact provides an easy explanation for one of the fundamental properties of genetic material—namely, its capacity for self-duplication. If the individual strands in such a double helix separate from one another, each strand can only be complemented by the precise corresponding sequence, which can be assembled from the free nucleotide subunits present in the surrounding medium. The stringing together of units into a coherent strand requires the activity of a particular enzyme, but we shall not be concerned further with this problem in our present context.

Although it is clear in general outline that the sequence of nucleotide bases in the DNA could determine a sequence of amino acids in a corresponding protein, the exact way in which this is done has turned out to be fairly complicated. Here there is only space to summarize the general conclusions that have been arrived at. Proteins, with very few exceptions, are built up as strings composed of sequences of twenty different amino acids. It is clear then that one nucleotide in a DNA would not suffice to determine one amino acid in a corresponding protein, since there are only four of the former while there are twenty of the latter. There must therefore be some kind of genetic "code," in which a *group* of nucleotides in DNA corresponds to a single amino acid in the protein. Most of the existing evidence is consistent with the idea that the effective groups in the nucleic acid contain three nucleotides. The code is a "triplet" code. The production of a string of amino acids corresponding to the sequence of nucleotides is spoken of as the "translation" of the code.

Before saying anything further about this, it is necessary to point out that there is an intermediate compound, which plays a role between a DNA and the final proteins. This intermediate is another variety of nucleic acid. It is known as RNA because in each unit building block the sugar is ribose, whereas in DNA it is deoxyribose. In RNA, also, the base uridine takes the place of thymine. RNA, as we shall see, occurs in several different forms in cells, and each form has a different part to play. In the present connection the important variety is one that is formed under the direct control of the DNA, so that the sequence of bases in the RNA exactly corresponds to that in the DNA (with uridine substituted for thymine, as pointed out above). The process by which this type of RNA, known as messenger RNA, is produced by the DNA is referred to as "transcription" (Figure 2·4). After it is formed, it leaves the chromosomes and passes out into the cytoplasm and is the direct agent that controls the assemblage of amino acids in the proteins.

It has been found that various synthetic RNA's, made by forming sequences of nucleotides in the laboratory, can act like messenger RNA in controlling the assemblage of amino acids into long strings. This has been one of the main ways of investigating the precise nature of the genetic code. It was found first, for instance, that a polynucleotide composed wholly of uridine residues (that is, the sequence –UUUUUU–) controls the joining together only of phenylalanine residues, to form a "protein" made up wholly of this amino acid. Thus it can be concluded that triplet UUU corresponds to phenylalanine. However, the situation is not absolutely clear-cut as yet. It seems fairly certain that several different triplets (for example, UUU and UUG) may correspond to the same amino acid, and the possibility is not entirely ruled out that sometimes one triplet such as UUU may correspond to phenylalanine and in somewhat different circumstances perhaps to another amino acid such as leucine. But although the details of the code are not yet

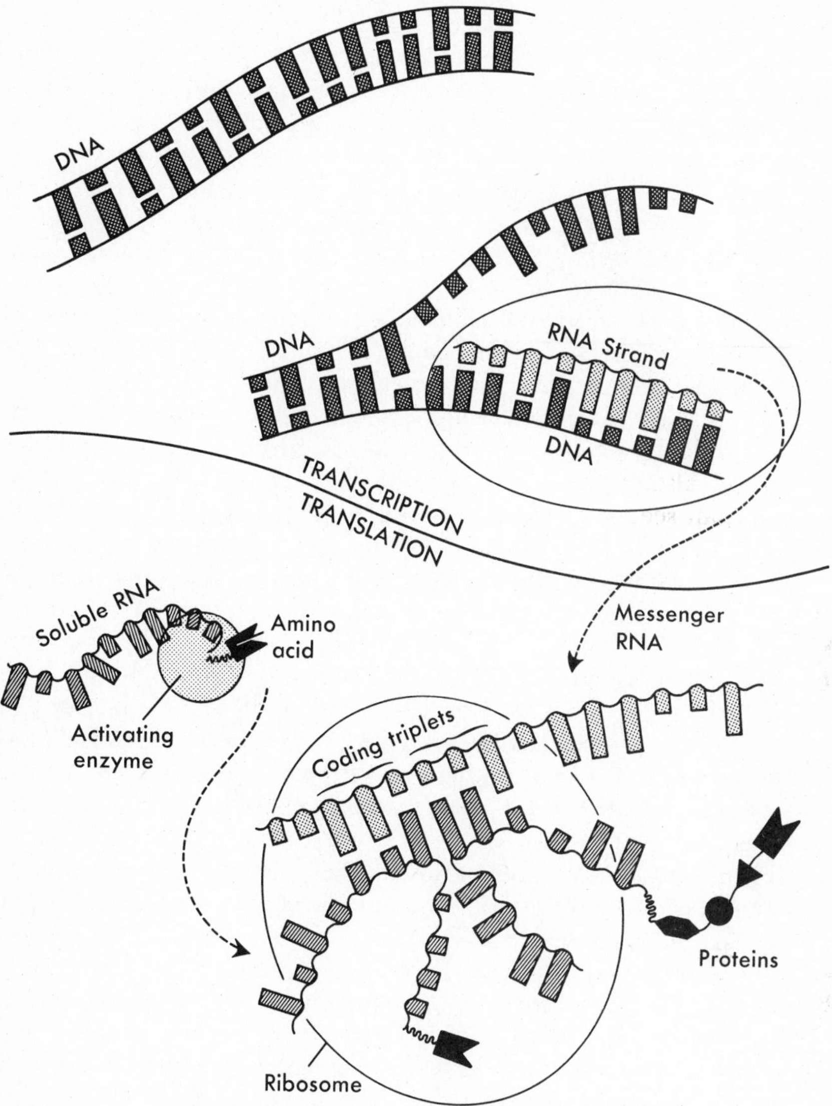

Figure 2·4. Main stages in the synthesis of a protein.

entirely agreed upon by everybody, it is already fairly certain that it operates according to the general principles just outlined.

There is, of course, a good deal more to the protein-synthesizing machinery of the cell than merely the DNA, the messenger RNA, and the amino acid building blocks. The assemblage of these amino acids into the protein takes place at certain small subcellular particles which can be seen with the electron microscope, known as ribosomes. Each ribosome is built of "ribosomal protein" and "ribosomal RNA," which differ from the messenger RNA and the protein that will be assembled along it. For the protein-synthesizing mechanism to be operative, it is also necessary for each amino acid to be combined with still another form of RNA, referred to as soluble RNA. This combination is brought about by "activating" enzymes. The system must also contain "polymerase" enzymes, which make the actual links between one amino acid and the next; and there must also be a source of energy in the form of the phosphate compounds that biological systems normally use to channel energy into the chemical reactions that enzymes are directing. When all these elements of the system are together and operating, the ribosomes become attached to the messenger RNA molecules; usually there are several ribosomes strung along each messenger RNA, forming groups known as polysomes. Apparently each ribosome works its way gradually along the messenger RNA from one end to the other, adding on the appropriate amino acid to the protein as it passes over each triplet sequence in the RNA.

The Molecular Biology of Embryos

The development of embryos, of all types from the simplest worms or sponges to the most complicated vertebrates, must be carried out by processes of the kind that molecular biology is beginning to discover. But the greatest advances in molecular biology have come, so far, from studies on very simple living systems, such as bacteria and viruses; and we have to keep ourselves open to the possibility—in fact, I would say, the probability—that there are many far-reaching new discoveries still to be made in higher organisms. The "molecular biological approach" has been applied to embryos only in the last few years. Some people might argue that its results at present are so tentative and incomplete that they should not be mentioned in an introductory book such as this; but they are so exciting and open so many new avenues of advance that they already form a part of the outlook of anyone to whom embryology is an alive and advancing subject, not a dead one. But be warned! What follows in this section may show you the kind of lines research is now following, but it will certainly be out of date before there is time to get it printed.

The basic apparatus that underlies embryonic development is the machinery by which genes control the synthesis of particular proteins. This starts with the sequence of nucleotides in the DNA of the chromosomes, and finishes with the sequence of amino acids in the proteins; most of the cogwheels in the intervening machine are built of RNA. There is the messenger RNA that is transcribed off the DNA; the RNA that is an essential part of the ribosomes at which the protein is eventually produced; and the soluble RNA that has to be attached to each amino acid before it can be built into the protein chain. Most of the studies that have so far been made on the molecular biology of embryos have depended on the few methods that are available for studying these various kinds of RNA. Essentially there are four basic methods:

1. *Autoradiography.* If a cell is offered one of its raw materials into which a radioactive atom is incorporated, the cell builds this, in the usual way, into its own structure. The cell can then be fixed, and if necessary sectioned; and we can place it in contact with a photographic film. Wherever there is a radioactive atom, ionizing radiations will be given off which will appear in the photographic emulsion, after that has been developed, as black dots. So we can trace where in the cell the various labeled raw materials go. However, the method cannot locate the materials quite as accurately as we should wish.

2. *Differential centrifugation.* A cell is allowed to incorporate radioactive raw material. It is then crushed, and the juice centrifuged. The heavier particles will be thrown down faster, the lighter more slowly; and by various means, such as centrifuging through a solution of sugar which is more concentrated and heavier at the bottom than the top, the discrimination between the particles in the cell juice can be made very sensitive.

3. *Stimulation of cell-free ribosomes.* Some RNA acts as "messenger" and, if it is added to a suitable preparation of isolated ribosomes, can cause them to start synthesizing the corresponding protein. (Please do not overlook how much skill, intelligence, and sheer intuition are hidden in that little word "suitable"; many people are devoting their lives to making these experiments "go.")

4. *Molecular hybridization.* One of the most far-reaching, but also most recent, of the experimental methods depends on the fact that an RNA that has been transcribed from a piece of DNA can, under "suitable" conditions, be persuaded to go back and stick to the DNA that made it much more strongly than to any other DNA. This gives a method of identifying the RNA messenger that corresponds to any particular DNA gene.

What has been discovered in embryos so far by the use of these methods? Only a tiny fraction of what is certainly going to be discovered in the next few years. This is one of the great breakthrough points. Actually much of the work to date has concentrated on the earliest and simplest phases of development, those leading up to, and just following, fertilization. During this period, most eggs do not synthesize many new ribosomes. They have to do this later, to provide the machinery for the intense protein synthesis necessary to produce muscle, blood, nerve cells, and so on. But for some time after fertilization, both amphibian and sea urchin eggs seem to get along with the store of ribosomes that were laid down in the egg before fertilization. It is not till about the time of gastrulation that new ribosomes begin to be produced; and when they do so, it is noteworthy that a nucleolus (which had been absent earlier) puts in an appearance in the nucleus. The evidence from autoradiography is strong that the nucleolus is concerned in the synthesis of ribosomal RNA. In a few special cases—for instance, in the toad Xenopus and the genetically well-analyzed fruit fly Drosophila—it is possible to breed strains with abnormal numbers of nucleoli (0, 1, 3, or 4, as well as the usual condition of 2). By "hybridizing" ribosomal RNA with the DNA from these strains, one can get an estimate of how much of the DNA in the nucleus is concerned with producing the RNA of the ribosomes; it turns out to be about 0.2 per cent.

During the period just after fertilization, when no ribosomal RNA is being produced, any radioactive raw material for RNA that is offered to the egg will be incorporated into one of the other varieties—either into messenger RNA or into soluble RNA. The soluble RNA is very light, and can be easily separated from the messenger by the centrifuge method. And then one can try to analyze the remaining, heavier (one hopes, messenger) RNA, by the most refined centrifugation techniques, by stimulation of isolated ribosomes, by hybridization, and so on. The subject is at this time as stimulating, as effervescent, and as difficult to summarize in a coherent textbook fashion as a glass of champagne. Just how soon after fertilization do eggs start producing new messenger RNA's? The evidence seems to be tending toward saying "very soon." Do these messengers fall into a few sharply distinct classes of weight (in the centrifuge), or do they vary continuously over a large range? Some workers say yes to the first alternative. How long do they persist in the cell before being destroyed? Probably for longer than they do in bacteria. And only in the last few months, two laboratories, one in the United States and the other in the U.S.S.R., claim to have discovered a completely new kind of RNA particle in early eggs, composed of messenger RNA combined with protein, occurring in a number of distinct weight classes smaller than ribosomes; and they propose calling them "informosomes."

In all this turmoil of new observations, which will have to be checked and repeated again and again before we know just which ones will stand up, there are already one or two points that do seem to be firmly established. Perhaps the most important—because it implies a matter of theoretical principle—is this. The ripe sea urchin egg sits around for quite a long time in a condition of dormancy. There is almost no synthesis of proteins or of RNA. As soon as it is fertilized, both processes start off rapidly. What had suppressed them in the unfertilized state? If the ribosomes are taken out of the unfertilized egg, they will synthesize proteins when stimulated by (somewhat unnatural) messengers; if the messengers of the unfertilized eggs are rather roughly treated, they will stimulate protein synthesis in healthy ribosomes. Exactly what is wrong in the unfertilized egg is still obscure; probably there are two blocks, one at the ribosomes and one at the messengers. But the point of principle is that here we have a control over the activity of genes in directing protein synthesis, which operates not by preventing the gene being transcribed into messenger RNA, but by preventing the RNA being effectively translated into protein. We shall see later (page 61) a neat example of "transcription control" in bacteria; we have to remember that, at any rate in more highly evolved organisms, there are also examples of "translation control."

In fact, the other main type of egg that has been studied so far, the amphibian, provides another example that reinforces this point. Here, protein synthesis just after fertilization is limited, not by controlling gene transcription into messenger RNA, but by the fact that there is not enough soluble RNA present to allow all the ribosomes to operate at full efficiency. We have to be prepared, then, to find our embryos using all sorts of different methods to control the effectiveness of the genes they contain.

Unfortunately, molecular biologists have not yet succeeded in working out methods of studying the more exciting periods of development, when the various parts of the animal are branching off into different developmental pathways. We have some good evidence that the messengers produced in the adult brain and liver are different; but just when do they first become different, and how? To what extent is the difference in proteins in a muscle cell as compared with a pancreas cell dependent on control of transcription or of translation? The techniques of molecular biology are only just getting ready to come to grips with these basic problems.

Meanwhile, embryologists have quite a lot to say about them. And to this we must now return.

Cell Biology

The older embryology depended far more on visual examination, with the microscope, than on chemical analysis. But there is nowadays a new look in this connection also. The enormous magnification possible with the electron microscope now makes it possible to see the ribosomes and often to verify that they are joined together in polysome packets. In the most favorable cases it is even possible to detect the messenger RNA strings to which they are attached. The protein that is being synthesized has not been seen as yet, probably because it immediately coils itself into a tight ball which is less easy to detect than the elongated strand of RNA.

The electron microscope also shows the presence of many other structures within cells whose functions, in protein synthesis and the general processes of development, are not yet by any means clear. For instance, in most cells, but not in all, the polysomes lie on the surface of internal membranes. This system of membranes, known as the endoplasmic reticulum, is not made up only of proteins but contains a large amount of fatlike (lipid) substances. The endoplasmic reticulum is often absent or only sparsely represented in very early embryonic cells and begins to put in a massive appearance just at the time the cells are starting to form their characteristic adult compounds. Further, it often has a quite different structure in different types of cells. These points suggest that it is very closely connected with the processes of cellular differentiation. It is, however, not yet clear whether the endoplasmic reticulum plays any controlling role in helping to guide the differentiation of cells into particular channels, or whether it is merely an end result expressing the kind of differentiation that has already been achieved.

The cytoplasm of cells also contains an important category of structures known as mitochondria. These are bodies of very variable shape but always containing many internal membranes. Many of the respiratory enzymes of the cell, concerned with transfer of energy from one chemical compound to another, are contained in the mitochondria and are probably arranged in a rather precisely organized manner on the internal membranes. Again, within the cytoplasm of developing cells one can usually find a closely packed mass of flattened sacs and vesicles, known as the Golgi apparatus. This is usually particularly well developed in cells that are secreting something—that is, producing a substance that they then pass out into the external medium. The Golgi apparatus seems to be mainly a means of providing transport for substances rather than playing any part in determining what these substances shall be.

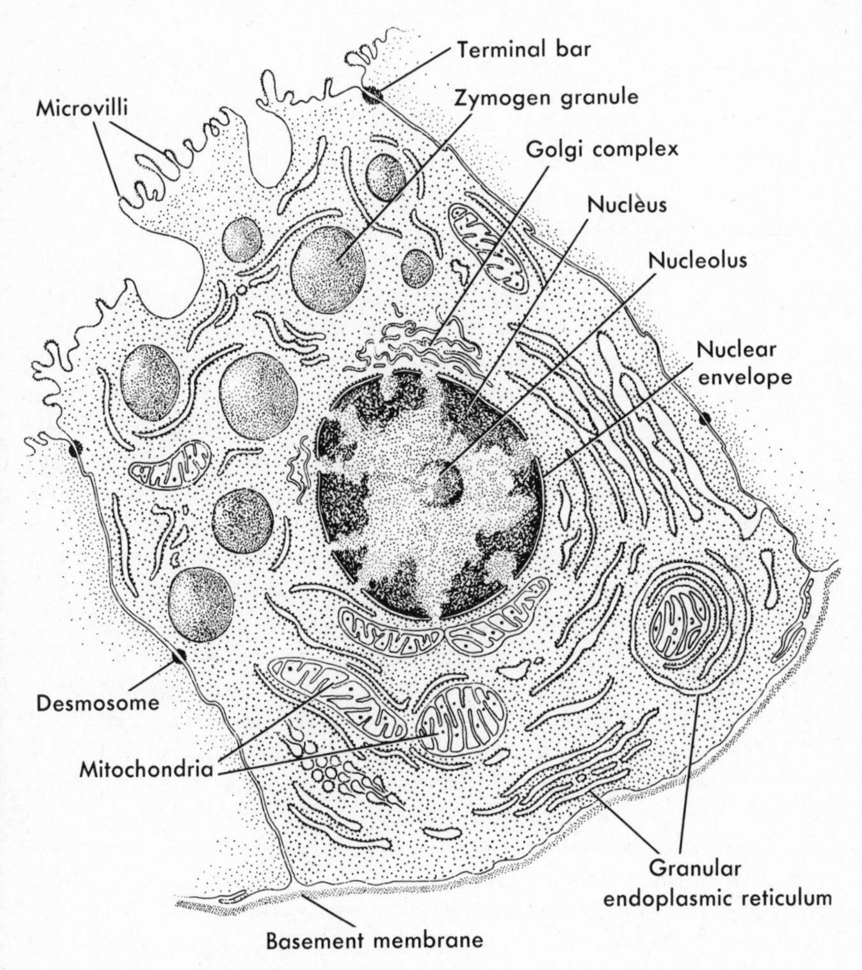

Figure 2·5. Section of a secretory cell as seen in the electron microscope.

One structure within cells that seems likely to be of great importance is the nuclear envelope. This disappears at the time of cell division, but for all the rest of the life of the cell it completely surrounds the hereditary material in the chromosomes, and must to some extent at least provide a barrier between this and the rest of the cell. In the electron microscope the nuclear envelope appears in cross section as two dark lines with a more transparent space between them, while in surface view it shows the structure of roughly circular rings or pores. It may be that these pores are in some cases completely open, so that substances could pass through them from inside the nucleus to the outside. Possibly this is the way in which the messenger RNA is passed out into the cytoplasm. It is noteworthy, however, that in many developing cells it can be seen that the outer member of the nuclear envelope folds outward and becomes part of the endoplasmic reticulum. The significance of this is not clear, but it suggests that there may be other methods of communication between the interior of the nucleus and the rest of the cell, besides the passage of the relatively small messenger RNA molecules, which we have considered above.

As we shall see later, developing embryos present us with difficult problems concerning the organization and coordination of the activities of many genes simultaneously. It is not easy to explain these on the supposition that all the genes operate by producing their own individual messenger RNA, quite disconnected from that coming from any other gene. It may possibly be—but this is still a mere speculation—that these outfoldings of the nuclear envelope into the endoplasmic reticulum are in some way concerned with the organization of gene activities.

The nucleus, of course, contains the chromosomes. The electron microscope has been disappointing in revealing relatively little new about their structure, and in this summary of recent advances there is little to be added to the accounts given in any elementary textbook of genetics. The most detailed knowledge we have of chromosome structure comes from observations with the light microscope of certain gigantic chromosomes, such as those in the salivary glands of insects and the oocytes of some animals. These are considered more fully on pages 38 and 65.

Within the nucleus also is a body known as the nucleolus. Again the electron microscope does not tell us very much about it, except that it is composed of ribonucleoprotein granules, which seem to be usually somewhat larger than the ribosomes. It appears at one or a few definite places on the chromosomes, which are known as nucleolar organizers. The nucleolus is certainly concerned with the RNA metabolism of the cells. In some cases it has been shown to be the place at which the soluble RNA is manufactured, and in early embryonic cells the ribosomal materials are also made there.

Embryonic cells also contain several other important types of particles. In the early embryos there are, for instance, nearly always supplies of yolk. This takes a number of different forms in different groups of animals. It is usually in the form of particles, sometimes of several different kinds, containing protein, lipid, and carbohydrate. These are often regarded as mere inert supplies of nutritive material, to serve the young embryo before it can feed for itself. However, there is some reason, which we shall discuss later on page 88, to believe that yolk contains substances that play a more important part in development than merely serving as raw materials for growth.

In the cytoplasm of many cells there are also various kinds of granules, usually bounded with definite membranes and often containing a number of smaller vesicles within them. Some of these particles are known to confer particular developmental properties on the cytoplasm in which they lie; for instance, particles of this kind characterize the region of the egg that will develop into the germ cells in certain types of insects. In other cases the particles probably contain enzymes which, if they are released by the breakdown of the external membrane, may profoundly change the whole metabolic system of the cell. These so-called lysosomes are like little time bombs waiting in the cytoplasm to be set off. Finally in many eggs there are stacks of "annulated lamellae"—that is to say, areas of membraneous material carrying a system of pores that resemble those on the nuclear envelope, and stacked on top of one another like loosely piled cards. It is possible that they originate from the nuclear envelope, but this is not yet certain, and their function is quite unknown.

Finally, it is worth mentioning that more and more evidence is accumulating for the existence of some type of genelike bodies in the cytoplasm, which can control and transmit hereditary characters. It has been claimed for many years that such bodies must occur in plants, where their effects can sometimes be seen on the chlorophyll-containing plastids. More recently people are coming to the conclusion that they may be commoner and more important than previously thought in cells in general. It seems rather likely that they have powerful effects on mitochondria and perhaps on other organelles. If so, we must expect to find that we shall have to take them into account in developmental processes. It is not yet known whether they consist of DNA or RNA (or, indeed, of nucleic acid at all, though that seems probable).

CHAPTER

3

Histogenesis or Differentiation in Time

IN THE LIGHT MICROSCOPE, early embryonic cells usually look as though they are rather "simple" objects, mere blobs of living substance, while the cells from adult tissues look "complex," with more specific shapes and with contents that may stain specifically with particular dyes or exhibit an elaborate structure, like the contractile fibrils of a muscle cell or the elaborate detail of some sensory or secretory cells (Figure 3·1). But this appearance of early simplicity and later complexity is probably largely deceptive. Early embryonic cells, particularly the egg cell itself, must contain very many different substances, not only all the enzymes required for general metabolism, but also many specific substances that will be involved in the developmental processes that will occur during differentiation toward the adult condition. During the formation of many types of eggs—particularly of the yolky eggs of vertebrates such as fish, amphibians, and birds—one can see signs of intense activity at very many places along the chromosomes. The chromosomes become unraveled into the form of a main strand with side loops, so that they resemble the old-fashioned "lampbrushes," which were used to clean the glasses of kerosene lamps (Figure 3·2). The loops consist mainly of protein, with some RNA. There are certainly several hundred of them, presumably all different; and some authors claim that every gene goes through the phase of loop production while the egg is maturing. It is not quite certain what happens to the materials formed on the loops, but it would be surprising if they did not remain somewhere hidden in the egg. In any case, after the lampbrush phase is over, there is another period, just before the egg finally ripens, in which it manufactures another lot of RNA, which is probably messenger RNA. Thus the egg is certainly more complex in constitution than appears at first sight.

Differentiation of cells to the adult condition is therefore not just a matter of getting more complicated. In fact some adult cells are certainly simpler than eggs. The most obvious example is the

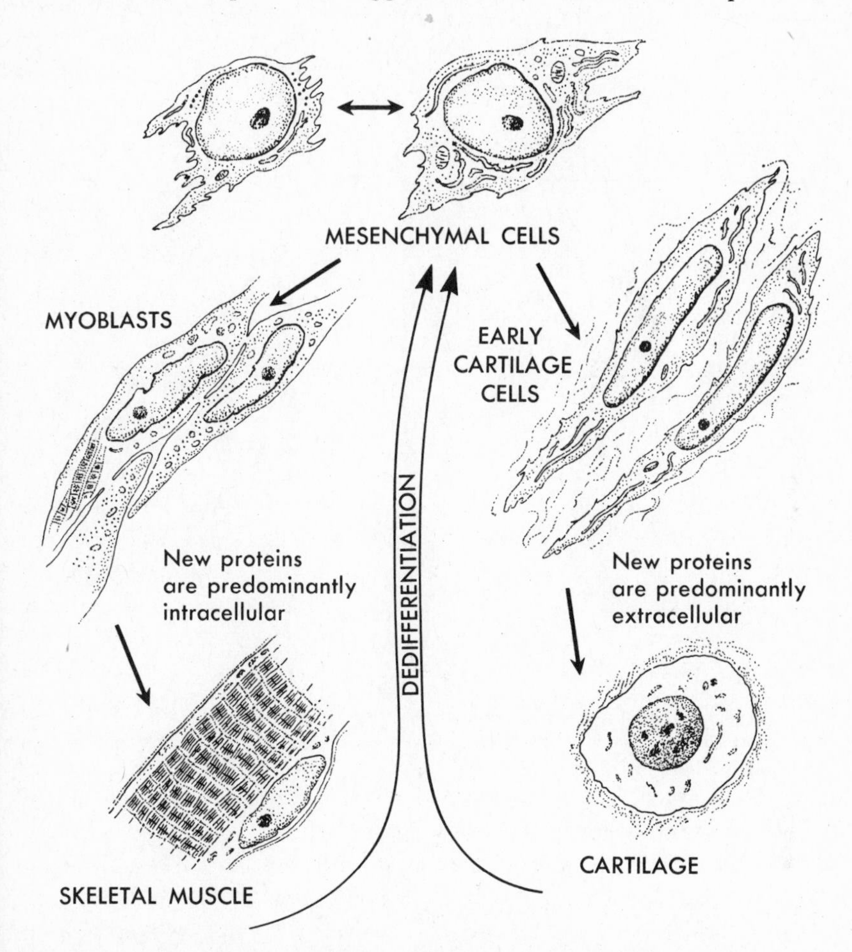

Figure 3·1. Differentiation of mesoderm cells from an early generalized "mesenchyme" type into two quite different specialized varieties—muscle cells and cartilage cells.

adult blood cell in mammals, which consists of little more than a cell membrane enclosing a solution of hemoglobin—even the nucleus disappears, and cell respiration and general metabolism almost cease. Few other adult cells reach this extreme simplicity, but it is approached by muscle cells, which contain little more than contractile proteins and mitochondria, and by some secretory cells that specialize in the production of particular products.

But although egg cells contain a large number of different substances, it is doubtful if they contain the molecules that are most characteristic of the various adult tissues, such as hemogloblin, muscle contractile proteins, insulin, the digestive enzymes secreted by the stomach, the light-sensitive pigments of the eye. If the egg

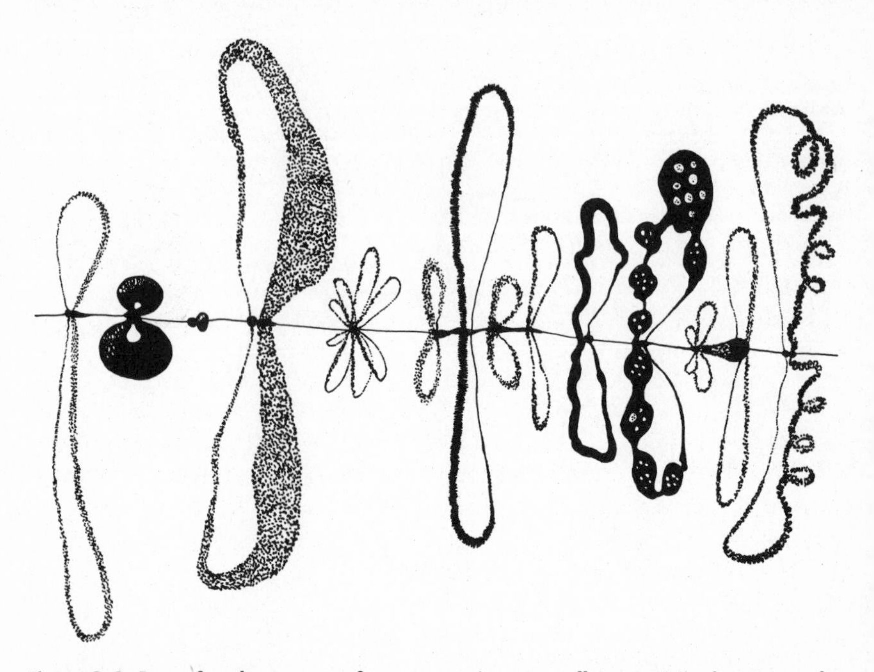

Figure 3·2. Part of a chromosome from a growing egg cell (oocyte) in the ovary of a salamander showing some of the variety of different kinds of "lampbrush loops" that are formed along the chromosome.

contains any of these, it possesses such minute quantities that they cannot be detected. Differentiation, even when it involves overall simplification of the cells, does depend on the production in massive quantities of substances of which the egg contains either none or minimal amounts.

These new substances are of many different kinds—fats, carbohydrates, proteins, pigments, and so on. The synthesis of all these substances is controlled by enzymes; and enzymes are always proteins. Proteins are, therefore, the most basic of all the substances produced in cells, and for a first approach to the problems of the changes in cellular constitution during development, it is sufficient to focus our attention on the synthesis of proteins.

It was pointed out previously (page 24) that proteins consist of sequences of amino acids joined together in long strings and that the order in which the amino acids are arranged is determined by the order of triplets of nucleotides in the DNA of the corresponding

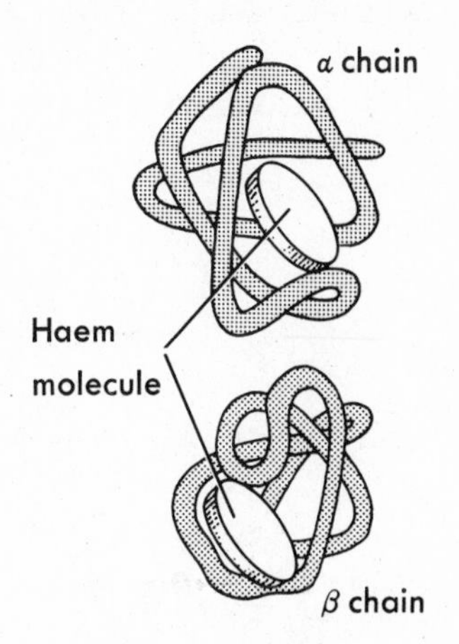

Figure 3·3. Models of the alpha and beta chains of hemoglobin. Each chain includes one flat disc-shaped heme molecule. Normally the two chains are packed closer together than shown here and are also associated with two other similar chains to make a composite body containing four subunits.

gene. It is now time to fill out this general statement with some concrete details. We will consider first the protein hemoglobin, which gives the red color to human blood. A fully formed molecule of normal hemoglobin is made up of four subunits. There are two subunits each consisting of a strand of a so-called α-hemoglobin and two further subunits each consisting of a different hemoglobin strand, known as β-hemoglobin. The strands are not stretched out in an elongated form, but are crumpled together in an elaborate but definite tangle, which has recently been described in detail, by x-ray crystallographic analysis (Figure 3·3). All four tangles of thread are bundled together into a composite body making the final hemoglobin molecule.

These molecules are under direct genetic control, and we know several genes in man that can alter their characteristics. For instance, there is a gene, known as the sickle cell gene, mutations of which cause alterations in one of the amino acids in the β chains. In normal hemoglobin the sixth amino acid from one end of the β chain is glutamic acid. The sickle mutant causes a valine to be in this place instead of glutamic acid. This is a very clear example of the way in which the gene controls the precise structure of the amino acid chain in a corresponding protein. The change in the gene DNA has not yet been determined in this case; presumably some triplet of bases has been altered from the form corresponding to glutamic acid to the form corresponding to valine. (The sickle cell gene is also interesting because individuals who are heterozygous for it, and therefore have some sickle cell as well as some normal hemoglobin, show some resistance of the blood corpuscles against the malaria parasite. Presumably for this reason the gene is rather common in populations such as those in West Africa and other places that have existed for many generations in regions where malaria is common. This is an example of natural selection at work.)

Genes and Proteins

The production by genes of precisely corresponding proteins is the basic mechanism by which gradual changes of histogenesis are brought about, but a little further study of hemoglobin begins to reveal some of the complexities that arise. In the first place, it is rather surprising to find that in the normal development of man different forms of hemoglobin are formed one after the other. In the early embryo there appears a form known as fetal hemoglobin. This contains two α chains like those in the adult hemoglobin, but instead of the β chains it has two of a quite different γ chain, the formation of which is controlled by another gene different from that controlling the β chains. The fetal hemoglobin is manufactured in blood cells that arise mainly in the liver of the embryo. It is only at a later stage that the β gene becomes active and produces the β chains that go to make up the adult hemoglobin, mainly in the red blood cells themselves which are formed in the bone marrow.

Now we have to ask, what causes this cessation of activity of the γ gene and the entry into activity of the β gene? In fact, we must go further and ask, why are not both these genes, and the α gene as well, active all the time? All the cells of the embryo, from the time of the fertilized egg onward, contain these genes, but so far as we can see none of them is active at all in the very earliest stages, and it is only after some time that the α and γ genes are, as it were, switched on and begin producing fetal hemoglobin; later the γ gene is usually switched off and the β gene becomes active, and the adult hemoglobin is produced. In some circumstances, in mutant individuals, a single cell may produce both types of hemoglobin, so that in them the α, β, and γ genes must all be active. The switching on or off of genes is obviously one of the fundamental problems of development. The next chapter will be mainly concerned with it.

We will now pass to a slightly more complex example of the

genetic control of proteins, in this case of enzymes. Many of the changes involved in histogenesis require an orderly sequence of steps, by which some simple compound is gradually elaborated into something more complicated. Many such sequences have been fully studied and their genetic control analyzed. This is particularly easy with organisms such as molds or bacteria, which are able to take simple substances out of the medium in which they are growing and gradually build them up into the more complicated chemical compounds required for growth. If a mutation occurs that alters and renders inactive one of the enzymes concerned with some step in the sequence of processes, then the product required for further growth cannot be formed: the organism will be unable to grow and multiply unless it is supplied from outside with this product, or at least with something that it is still capable of converting into it.

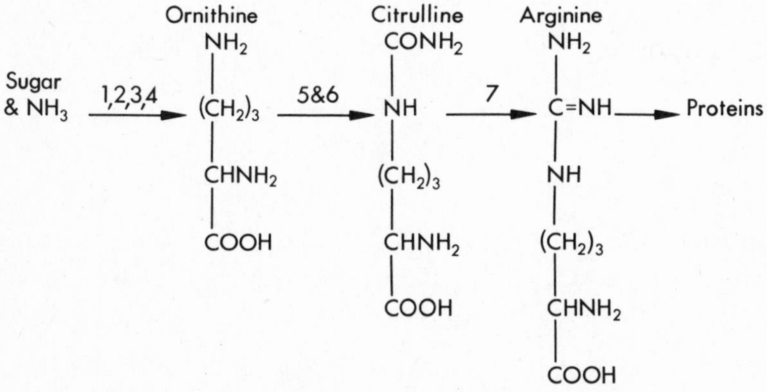

$$\text{Sugar} \;\&\; NH_3 \xrightarrow{1,2,3,4} \text{Ornithine} \xrightarrow{5\&6} \text{Citrulline} \xrightarrow{7} \text{Arginine} \longrightarrow \text{Proteins}$$

Ornithine: $NH_2 - (CH_2)_3 - CHNH_2 - COOH$

Citrulline: $CONH_2 - NH - (CH_2)_3 - CHNH_2 - COOH$

Arginine: $NH_2 - C{=}NH - NH - (CH_2)_3 - CHNH_2 - COOH$

Figure 3·4. Some steps in the synthesis of arginine.

For instance, in the mold Neurospora, the important amino acid arginine is synthesized through a sequence of steps, some of which are shown in Figure 3·4. A number of genes, numbered 1 to 7, are known that control the formation of the enzymes that act at the successive steps in the sequence. If the mold has a mutated allele at a gene (5 or 6) controlling the step from ornithine to citrulline, this chemical reaction cannot occur, and no arginine can be produced. Growth therefore ceases, and the mold soon dies, unless either arginine or citrulline is supplied to it. If, in some other strain, the citrulline to arginine enzyme (7) is abnormal, adding citrulline to the culture medium does not suffice; only arginine will do.

This is a good example of an enzyme sequence. It is, in fact, only a small part of the much more elaborate sequences that must be involved when a developing cell converts the simple raw materials with which it usually has to deal into the highly elaborate end products that characterize its adult state. Some of the other synthetic steps connected with the glutamic acid to arginine sequence are shown in Figure 3·5. Further, Neurospora can live in a medium in which it has to obtain all its carbon from acetate and all its nitrogen from ammonia or nitrate, and there will have been many synthetic steps before these simple compounds are converted into glutamic acid. At the same time the same raw materials have been converted into a number of other elaborate organic com-

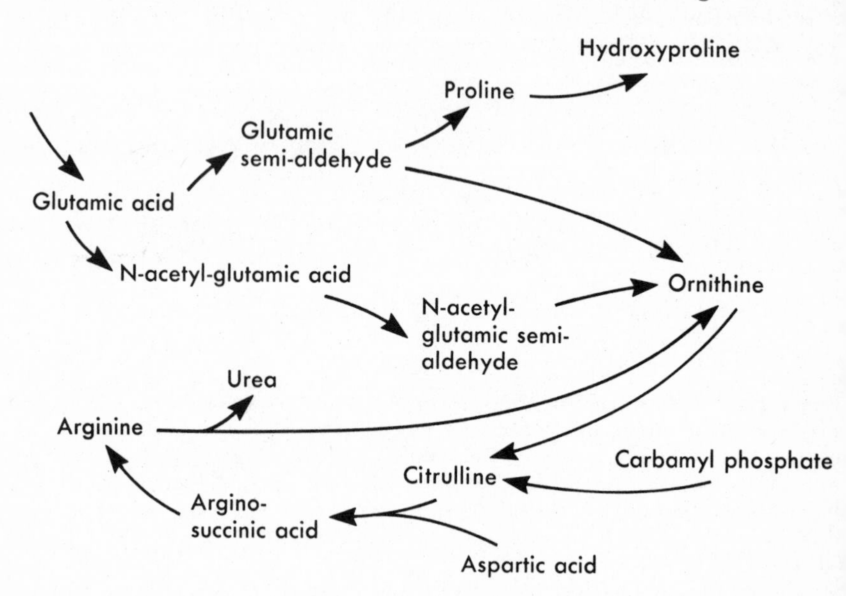

Figure 3·5. Some other synthetic steps connected with the glutamic acid to arginine sequence.

pounds, by still other enzymes. The whole synthetic system of the cell must, therefore, be a very elaborate network, rather than just a collection of sequences that always remain quite isolated from one another.

In such a network there will be many types of interaction between the different processes. In some cases one and the same material may be convertible by different enzymes into two different products. Again, one and the same enzyme may be able to act on two different compounds. There is a further, at first sight rather unexpected but particularly interesting, type of interaction which occurs within sequences such as those in diagram in Figures 3·4 and 3·5. It has been found that quite often the end product of such a sequence of reactions inhibits the activity of an enzyme that operates at one of the earlier steps. This phenomenon is known as "end-product inhibition." The result of it is that if the end product is supplied from outside, it inhibits an early enzyme involved in its own synthesis, and thus the cell does not synthesize any more of the compound. This is presumably advantageous to the cell, which does not waste energy in making something that it is already receiving from elsewhere. Thus one can imagine how this system has been built up during evolution by natural selection.

The mechanism by which end product inhibition operates has been extensively investigated. Enzymes are proteins that are folded together into a tangle in such a way that their surface contains

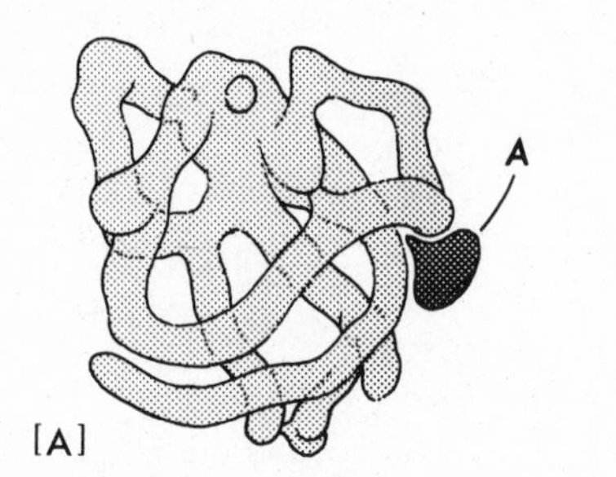

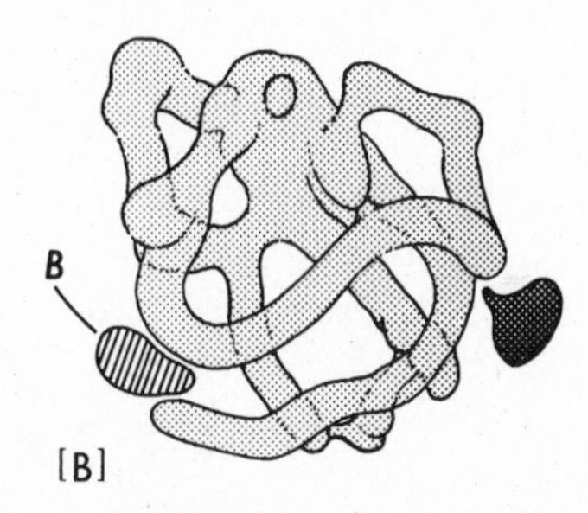

Figure 3·6. The concept of an allosteric enzyme. A: When a protein operates as an enzyme the substrate molecules fit into certain active sites on its surface as is suggested at *A*. (We do not yet know in detail the structure of any single enzyme; the protein molecule drawn in the figure is based on that of myoglobin as worked out by Kendrew.) **B:** The enzyme molecule is "allosteric" if it possesses some other site, such as *B*, and if the properties of site *A* are altered when an appropriate molecule is attached to *B*.

certain regions that react with the small molecules that become altered during the enzyme reaction. Such reactive regions on the surface of the enzyme are known as active sites. Now in most cases the end product that inhibits the enzyme reaction does not itself react with the active site where the enzyme reaction occurs. It seems to attach itself to the enzyme molecule at some other point on the surface, and by this attachment to cause a change in shape of the enzyme so that the active site is deformed and no longer reacts in the normal way. Enzymes that can behave in this way must, in fact, have two reacting regions: one at which the reaction they catalyze occurs, and another at which they interact with the inhibiting molecule. Enzymes (or other large molecules) that have two reacting regions, and in which the properties of one region depend on the conditions at the other, are referred to as "allosteric" (Figure 3·6). The present opinion is that molecules with allosteric properties play a very important role in regulating and organizing the changes in chemical constitution that go on in developing cells (see page 82).

The Development of Cells, Tissues, and Organs

The discussion so far has dealt only with development at the simplest level relevant to biology, that of biochemical substances. This is really the province more of geneticists than of embryologists. The student of embryos is faced with the need to understand how a part of the egg turns into the liver, another part into the brain, a third part into a forearm, and so on. These developments are, of course, based on chemical changes, but they amount to something much more complicated than that. They are alterations in elaborately organized complex systems, and mere conventional chemistry is not enough to give an account of them, any more than it could account for the evolution of a Model "T" Ford (an "embryonic" motor vehicle) into a Thunderbird roadster on the one side or a rocket transporter on the other (to give two examples of specialized motor vehicles corresponding to adult cells).

In approaching the problems of the development of cells and organs we have still to base ourselves on the fundamental postulate that the nature of the changes that occur will be ultimately dependent on genes. The new point we have to consider is that we shall be dealing with parts of the developing body which are affected by very many genes. Nobody knows exactly how many genes are active in the development of any type of cell, but it is probably several hundred. Presumably even more would be involved in the development of any fairly complicated organ, but nobody has recently made a serious attempt to find out. The fullest description we have of the large range of genes affecting the development of an organ is a study made about a quarter of a century ago on the wings of the fruit fly Drosophila, which has been very extensively studied by geneticists. The developmental effects of about forty genes were described. It is worth summarizing briefly the main outlines of the story because some principles of general importance emerge from it (Figure 3·7).

The wing of a fly like Drosophila develops from a small bunch of cells, known as the imaginal bud, which lies in the body of the larva or grub. This begins to grow out into the wing at the time the larva turns into a pupa. We shall discuss later, in the next chapter, what causes these cells to develop into a wing rather than something else. Here we will assume that this decision has been made and that wing development starts. When it begins the imaginal bud is in the form of a hollow bag, one side of which is thicker than the other. The thick side becomes folded in toward the center of the bag and begins to grow rapidly, so that it soon

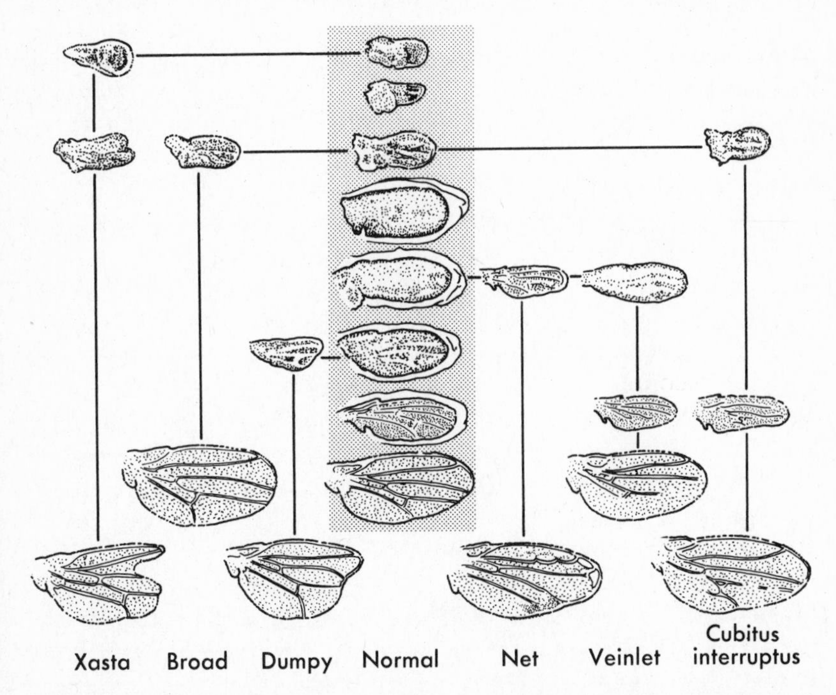

Figure 3·7. Genetic control of the development of the Drosophila wing. Stages in the normal development of the wing are shown in the eight drawings down the center of the figure. From the imaginal bud at the top, through stages of enlargement by cell division (next two figures), expansion by the internal pressure of body fluid (fourth figure), then renewed contraction during which the final veins appear (next three figures), leading to the formation of the final adult wing (shown on a smaller scale). On the left are shown the effects of three genes that affect the general shape of the wing. *Xasta* affects the first formation of the wing in the imaginal bud. *Broad* affects the first expansion by cell-division. *Dumpy* causes an increased contraction. On the right are three genes affecting the veins. In *net* there is less contraction than usual and some extra veins appear. In *veinlet* the veins first appear in their normal form but the tips of them are later obliterated. In *cubitus interruptus* there is an abnormality in the first signs of the veins that appear during the growth phase.

bursts through the other thin side, which disappears. The folded area then flattens out into a leaflike blade, somewhat similar in shape to the final wing, though very much smaller in area. This blade begins to grow, at different rates along its length and across its width. During this period its base becomes attached to the surface of the body, so that the wing begins to stick out to the side of the animal. After a time the wing blade begins to become inflated: the body fluid (or blood) of the animal seems to be pumped into it, forcing the two surfaces apart and expanding the whole thing like an inflated rubber bag. This goes on until the wing blade becomes a thin-walled inflated sack. After that the internal pressure drops again, and the wing begins to contract, so that eventually it once more forms a flat blade. It is during this contraction that the wing acquires its final outline. As the internal fluid drains away, and the two surfaces of the wing blade come together, they come into complete contact with one another everywhere except for a few channels, which are arranged in a definite pattern. These are the so-called veins, which remain filled with blood and with a thickened surface even in the adult wing. The final stage of development is characterized by a great expansion in area of each of the cells. This expansion is so great that the wing is at first crumpled up into complicated folds. It is only after the final insect emerges from the pupa that body fluid is again pumped into the wings through the veins, and this expands the folds and stretches out the wing to its final flattened shape. Finally the wing dries out, presumably by simple evaporation of moisture from its surface. Its cells die and the wing is then in its final form.

Now we know genes that effect every one of these stages of development. In fact, for most stages we know several genes that are active. For instance, in the first stage of expansion and growth at the very beginning of the pupal period, there are some genes that increase the growth in length, others that increase the growth in width. Again at the time of inflation and contraction there are some genes that increase the inflation, others that increase the contraction. Throughout the whole of the development all these genes are interacting with one another in complicated ways. It is particularly important to notice that we can find many examples of genes that seem to act antagonistically to each other. The final shape of the wing is a compromise between genes that, for instance, tend to increase the inflation and genes that tend to increase the contraction; between genes that tend to cause an increase in length and those that cause an increase in width, and so on. The end result is a balance between many opposing forces.

The Canalization of Development

The Drosophila wing serves as an example to illustrate this point, but the principle is a very general one. Any organ such as a wing, a leg, or an eye must always be regarded as expressing some sort of compromise or balance between the conflicting or competing activities of very many genes.

It is particularly important to discover that these balances show a certain degree of stability, in the sense that it is quite difficult to persuade the developing system *not* to finish up by producing its normal end result. If something occurs that would tend to strengthen one of the factors (say, a tendency toward elongation), its effectiveness will be opposed by the conflicting tendencies (toward broadening and shortening) which will also be present in the system, and the net result will be less than we might have expected. In fact, unless the elongating tendency is very strong, the forces opposing it may swamp it out altogether, so that the final wing appears completely normal. This is the explanation, in developmental terms, of the phenomenon of dominance and recessivity which is so well known to geneticists. If, by producing a heterozygous individual, we reduce the dose of a gene from its usual level of two normal alleles to the lower level of one normal plus one mutant allele, we often find that this makes no difference to the appearance of the animal at the end of development. The whole developing system, involving interaction between many genes, has reacted so as to absorb the comparatively slight degree of abnormality produced by the single dose of the mutant allele. The balance is stable enough not to be disturbed. The system is to some extent "self-righting," like a well-designed automobile which has a tendency to straighten itself out after being put into a slight curve.

This self-righting tendency of development is seen in many contexts and at many levels of organization. It is, in fact, much more widely known and better recognized in embryological connections than in the field of genetics. Here are a few examples. As we shall see later, many eggs contain particular types of cytoplasm arranged at definite places within them. When such an egg is centrifuged the different types of cytoplasm may be displaced; but if such a centrifuged egg is left to itself it is usually found that there is a strong tendency for the cytoplasms to move back again to their original pattern. Exactly how this is done is still obscure. It seems usually to depend in some way on patterns of difference within the cell surface; possibly there are local regions of the cell surface with particular attractions for particular types of cytoplasm; but however it is done, the net result is a tendency for the egg to right itself after disturbance.

Again, if a piece is removed from an early egg, or even if the egg is cut in half, it is frequently found that the system rights itself, and a completely normal embryo is produced (see Figure 3·12). This happens in the human being, when two identical twins may be produced by one egg which in some way becomes effectively divided in two, so that each twin arises from what should have been only half the normal system. In many types of animal this kind of self-righting or "regulation" persists into much later stages long after the first few cell divisions. Even when it begins to be lost, lesser but still quite extensive regulation continues to occur. For instance, a half brain or a half limb may produce a whole organ, and even a quite small part of the embryo will often show some tendency to increase itself and form more than would have been expected.

The genetic basis for the regulatory processes seen in very early embryos has never been fully investigated, and it would be difficult to do so. However, it is quite possible to study the less impressive examples of resistance to disturbance that can be found in the later stages of development and to show that they depend on the properties of the genes contained in the organism. For instance, if we subject a developing embryo to some external agent (for example, temperature) that tends to make it produce an abnormal end result, we find that the degree to which it shows an effect of the treatment can be either increased or decreased by selective breeding. This is a proof that it is its genes that control its ability to absorb the abnormal treatment—that is, to right itself.

The general phrase for the property we have been discussing is "the canalization of development." The region of an early egg that develops into a brain or into a limb or any other organ follows some particular pathway of change. What we have found now is that these pathways are "canalized," in the sense that the developing system has an inbuilt tendency to stick to the path, and is quite difficult to divert from it by any influence, whether an external one like an abnormal temperature or an internal one like the presence of a few abnormal genes. Even if the developing system is forcibly made abnormal—for instance, by cutting part of it away—it still tends to get itself back onto the canalized pathway and finish up as a normal adult. The canalization is, of course, not complete. Developing systems do not always reach the fully normal adult state. The point is that they have a tendency to do so, and are not entirely at the mercy of any temporary abnormalities. It is easy to see why this may be a valuable property for animals developing in a very changeable world, and why natural selection should have built up systems of genes that interact in this self-stabilizing way which partly buffers out the effect of potentially harmful circumstances.

One can make a mental picture of the situation by thinking of the development of a particular part of an egg as a ball running down a valley. It will, of course, tend to run down to the bottom of the valley, and if something temporarily pushes it up to one side, it will again have a tendency to run down to the bottom and finally finish up in its normal place. If one thinks of all the different parts of the egg, developing into wings, eyes, legs, and so on, one would have to represent the whole system by a series of different valleys, all starting out from the fertilized egg but gradually diverging and finishing up at a number of different adult organs. Such a mental picture has been called the "epigenetic landscape" (Figure 3·8).

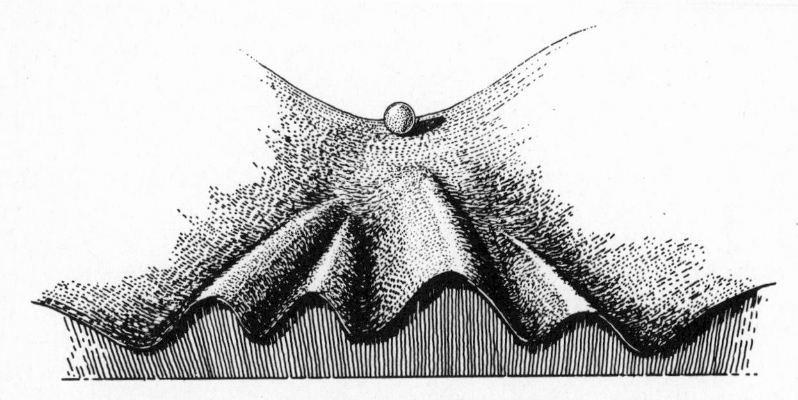

Figure 3·8. The epigenetic landscape. The various regions of a developing embryo have in front of them a number of possible pathways of development, and any particular part will be switched into one or other of these potential paths.

This "landscape" presents, in the form of a visual model, a description of the general properties of a complicated developing system in which the course of events is controlled by many different processes that interact in such a way that they tend to balance each other. If, for instance, process A for some reason becomes stronger than usual, this will have repercussions that will eventually cause some opposing process B to become stronger also, so that the overall balance remains much the same. Regulatory interactions of this kind are often spoken of nowadays as examples of "feedback," but that word actually has many senses. It is most properly used in situations such that, when process A tends to go faster than usual, secondary effects are produced that slow A down again. But this is by no means the only kind of regulation that occurs in embryonic systems. For instance, a mutant gene may genuinely produce an inefficient enzyme, and this does not produce any secondary effects that cause the enzyme to become more efficient; what happens is that the slack gets taken up somewhere else in the cell's biochemical system, and the overall result on the cell's total activity is minimized or even completely "buffered out."

Is Differentiation Reversible?

The epigenetic landscape immediately suggests several very important questions. First of all, how do the various parts of the egg get into the various valleys? How is it decided that one part of a Drosophila will develop into a wing, another part into a leg, and so on? This is the problem of "switch mechanisms"—that is, processes that switch development into one channel or another, or, to put the same thing in a different way, processes that switch on one group of gene activities rather than another group. This is the subject of the next chapter.

But there is another question we might discuss now. Once a part of the egg has got into a channel and traveled some distance along it toward becoming an adult organ like a limb or an eye, can it reverse its direction and go back again toward an embryonic condition? Or can it suddenly change out of this path of development and start becoming something quite different without going back on its tracks to an earlier condition? Is developmental change reversible or not? Do adult cells of one type (such as muscle cells or skin cells) still contain the potentialities that are needed to form cells of a different type (such as bone cells or nerve cells)?

If a group of partially differentiated cells are cut out from a late embryo and placed in a drop of a suitable nutritive medium, they often start growing much more rapidly than they had done in the body. The mass of cells gradually becomes looser, and individual cells creep out into the medium along the surface of the vessel in which they are placed. Such masses of cells, kept alive outside the body, are known as tissue cultures.

Under such conditions many early embryonic cells will continue their development and eventually become more differentiated (but see page 74). On the other hand, already differentiated cells usually lose many of the obvious signs of differentiation and appear to become much simpler (Figure 3·9). They take on one or another of three basic appearances, and look as if they had gone back toward an embryonic condition. This is, however, often somewhat deceptive. If, after a period in tissue culture in which the cells appear to have lost many of their signs of differentiation, they are put back again into the body of an animal, or into other conditions in which the group becomes tightly coherent once more, it is often found that the cells have in fact retained their differentiated character, and can soon begin to exhibit again all the signs of specialization they had had in the first place. There is still a good

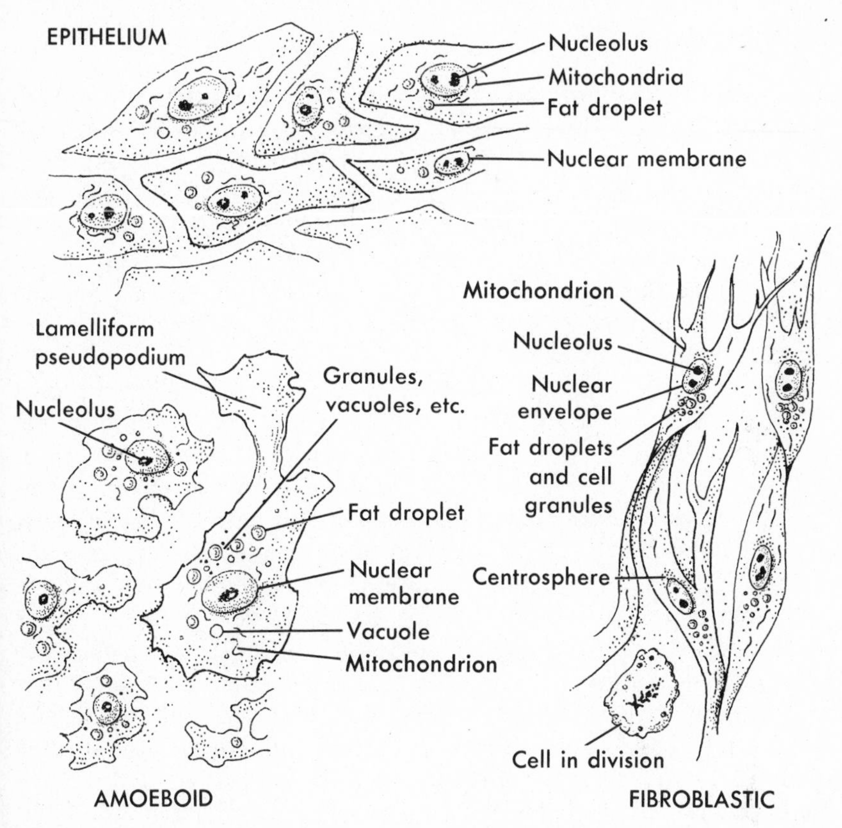

Figure 3·9. The three basic types of structure assumed by cells in tissue culture.

deal of argument whether they ever do become really de-differentiated or not. Some authors maintain that cells that are caused to grow rapidly, so that they undergo many cell divisions quickly one after the other, do actually lose their differentiation and regress to an embryonic condition, from which they can then be persuaded to differentiate once more into something quite different from what they had originally been.

There are other situations in which there is better evidence that at least some differentiated cells can be caused to lose their initial differentiation and then to develop along some other pathway. Some of the best cases of this occur during regeneration. In many animals, though unfortunately not in man, if a part of the body is removed, various processes go on by which a new part is grown to replace it. All these processes are known as regeneration, but the end result may be attained in a number of rather different ways. For instance, if the lens is removed from the eye of a frog or newt a small growth may appear in some other part of the eye and eventually develop into a new lens (Figure 3·10); sometimes it is formed from the retina, which is the layer of very specialized

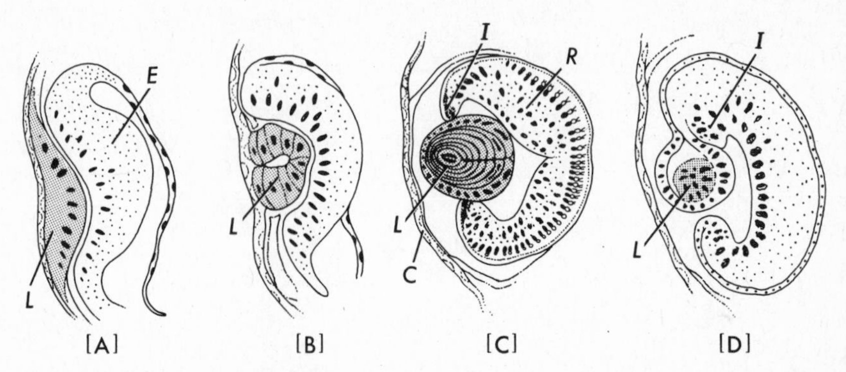

Figure 3·10. Lens development and regeneration. A—C: Three stages in the normal development of the eye in amphibians. The eyecup, *E*, grows out from the brain, and where it touches the ectoderm induces the latter to form a vesicle which becomes the lens, *L*. In **C**, *R* is the retina, derived from the eyecup, the edges of this being the iris (*I*); C is the cornea, developed from the ectoderm. If the lens is removed from such an eye, a new one may be regenerated from the retina or iris, as seen in **D**; it may also be produced from the cornea.

cells that actually receive the visual image in the eye, in other cases from the cornea, which is the transparent covering over the outer surface of the pupil. In both instances the lens is formed from cells that are originally highly differentiated, and they have to lose their initial differentiation and then develop again along a new pathway that leads to the formation of lens cells.

In most other instances of regeneration the first sign of the process is the accumulation at the surface of the wound of a small bundle of embryonic-looking cells. This little group of cells, known as a blastema, then begins to grow and gives rise to all the necessary parts to replace whatever has been amputated. For instance, if the hand and forearm of a newt's front leg are cut off, a blastema will form at the cut surface and eventually grow into just these parts of the forearm and hand that have been removed, neither more nor less. This is a very remarkable performance, which we shall mention when discussing morphogenesis in the last chapter.

The question we have to ask now is, where do the cells of the blastema come from? Many people have argued that in animals that can regenerate, the body contains a reserve supply of embryonic cells, which are scattered through the more differentiated cells but which retain their embryonic condition. When a wound is made these reserve cells are supposed to accumulate and form the blastema and then begin to differentiate. This does in fact occur in the regeneration of some invertebrates, such as flatworms, but in the vertebrates that can regenerate well, such as newts and salamanders, something more interesting is involved. In these animals, irradiation

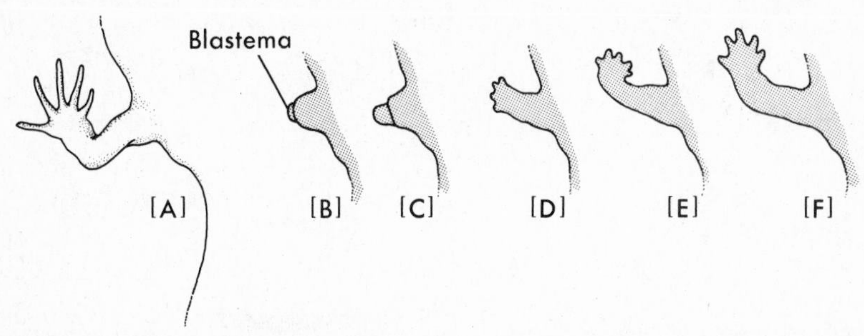

Figure 3·11. Regeneration. A: Outline of the hind limb of the crested newt. B–F: The first stages in the regeneration of the limb when it is amputated through the thigh region.

with x-rays, even if carried out some months before a limb is amputated, entirely prevents any regeneration (the reasons for this are still quite obscure). We can take an x-rayed animal, cut off its forelimb, wait long enough to be sure that no regeneration is going to occur, and then graft onto the stump an arm from another, nonirradiated newt. This grafted limb can heal on quite satisfactorily. After it has done so, it can be amputated in its turn, leaving only a small disc of unirradiated material attached to the stump on the x-rayed animal. At this stage, regeneration happens. This is very good evidence that the cells of the blastema, which grow into the new limb, are derived locally. It seems, in fact, that already differentiated skin cells, and probably muscle cells, at the site of the wound lose their differentiation and then constitute the blastema.

Moreover, in other experiments it has been shown that if the upper arm bone (humerus) is removed from a newt forelimb, it is not regenerated; but if this boneless arm is amputated, a regenerate grows out from the stump, and does contain a new humerus, although no normal bone-forming cells were present at the cut surface. This shows that the cells that form the blastema do really return, to some extent at least, to an embryonic condition, and differentiate again in other pathways. However, they do not seem to become completely embryonic so that they could develop into something quite foreign to their nature; for instance, attempts to persuade blastema produced on limbs to develop into tails have had very little success.

There is, then, rather good evidence that differentiation, at least along certain pathways, can under some circumstances be reversed. However, it is usually not at all easy to reverse it, although, as we have seen (page 12), the less definite differentiation of plant cells is much more flexible. But it is only in rather few cases that we know experimental methods of persuading animal cells that have once differentiated to go back to a more embryonic condition. It may be that certain types of differentiation—for instance, in nerve cells—are pretty well irreversible.

As we have been arguing all through this chapter, the changes of differentiation are caused by gene activities. Development along a particular pathway is brought about when certain particular genes are active. The cases in which we can show that differentiated cells can regress to an earlier condition, and then develop again in a different direction, demonstrate that, in these cases at least, the genes required for the second course of differentiation must still be present, even if they are not operating in first-course differentiation. In types of differentiation that are not reversible—or, at least, in which we cannot prove reversibility—it is possible that some of the genes whose activities are not required become completely inactivated, or even possibly lost from the cell altogether. This certainly occurs in some cases. For instance, during the development of the red blood cells of mammals the whole nucleus disappears after setting going the processes leading to the manufacture of hemoglobin. The final cell does not even contain the genes for doing this, let alone those necessary to differentiate into anything else. However, this is rather a special situation. There is very little evidence that genes are often lost from differentiated cells; it is much more probable that usually the difficulty in reversing differentiation is not that other genes have been lost but rather that the development involves such a complicated network of processes that it would be an extremely long and tricky process to unravel them. One could, in theory, take an automobile, dismantle it, and build the pieces up again with a little modification into two motorcycles, but it wouldn't be easy; and it is something like this that we are asking a differentiated cell to do when we try to persuade it to lose its present differentiation and develop into something else.

Nuclear Transplantation

From this point of view, it seems reasonable to expect that the developmental changes in the nucleus, which contains the genes but not much else, may be more easily reversed than the changes undergone by the cell as a whole. It would be easy to test this if

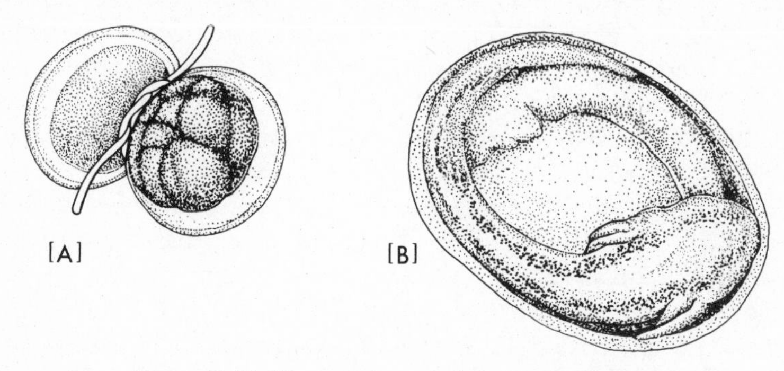

Figure 3·12. Spemann's constriction experiment.

the nucleus from one sort of differentiated cell could be transferred into the cytoplasm of another more embryonic cell, and one watched to see whether the nucleus could still carry out all the functions necessary for some other type of differentiation.

In practice this is not an easy result to achieve. The early embryologists were able, by a variety of methods, to introduce a nucleus into one of the specialized regions of cytoplasm contained in some eggs where it would not have been in normal development. For instance, if a newt's egg is constricted by a loop of hair, after fertilization but before it has divided into the first two cells, the nucleus will be confined to one of the two ends of the cell. It is only this end that divides in the first few cell divisions (Figure 3·12). Later, when the cells and the nuclei have become smaller, one of the nuclei may pass across the bridge into the other end, which then begins dividing in turn. Spemann found that if this passage across the bridge took place as late as the 16-cell stage, the region that at first had no nucleus might develop normally into all the organs of an adult. Since the arrangement of the cleavage nuclei is quite random, he drew the conclusion that any of the first 16 nuclei is as good as any other, and that they all have the capacity to control every type of differentiation.

This is not a very surprising conclusion when it applies only to the early nuclei formed by the first few cleavages. The real question arises about the potentialities of the later nuclei, taken from cells that have really started to differentiate. In recent years several embryologists have been successful in transferring the nuclei from some differentiated cells into more embryonic cytoplasm. So far this has been successfully done only on the embryos of frogs and toads. Surprisingly, the results in the two types of animals are rather different.

The method used has been to inject a nucleus sucked out of a late differentiated cell into an early uncleaved egg of the same species. One has, of course, to be sure that any differentiation that then takes place is under the control of the injected nucleus, and not under that of the egg's own nucleus. This nucleus can, however, be eliminated, either by physically removing it or by killing it with ultraviolet. Actually, in toads this is not necessary, since if the injected nucleus is put into an unfertilized egg, the egg's own nucleus plays no part in subsequent events, while the stimulus of pricking the egg to inject the nucleus is sufficient to make development start. In both frogs and toads it has been found that a nucleus taken from the early embryonic cells, up to the stage of the blastula, is usually capable of making possible complete development into a normal larva. But it has been found in frogs that the nuclei begin to lose their capacity to allow complete differentiation soon after the blastula stage. It appears that they undergo some change that cannot be reversed merely by placing the nucleus in the early egg cytoplasm.

These changes are, in fact, rather stable. A typical experimental result is shown in Figure 3·13. The first step is to take a number of nuclei from the endoderm of a late blastula and inject them into a series of enucleated eggs (only two are shown in the drawing, for simplicity, but actually many more were used). These recipient eggs are allowed to develop to the young blastula stage, and then from each egg another series of nuclear transplantations is made. The nuclei from each blastula should be exactly the same, since they were derived from one original transplanted nucleus. The animals into which they develop therefore form a "clone"—that is, a group of genetically identical individuals. It is found that the clones may differ, some giving full normal development, some producing

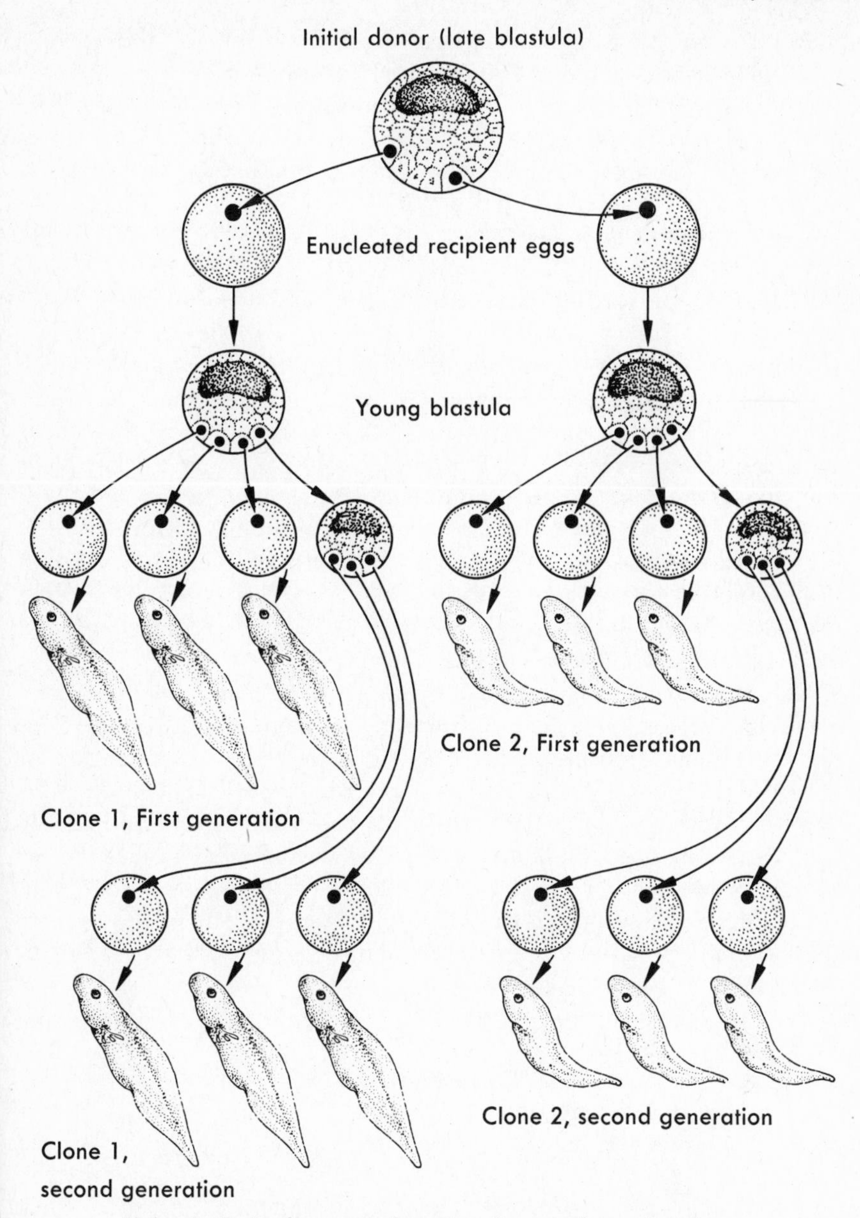

Figure 3·13. Nuclear transplantation. See text for explanation.

mainly, or entirely, misshapen and badly developed tadpoles. This shows that in the initial late blastula with which the experiment started, some nuclei had already lost some of the capacity to allow normal development to proceed. If one of the eggs in each clone is allowed to proceed only as far as the blastula stage, and is then used as a source for more nuclei for transplantation, one can get a second transplant generation. It is found that the character of the clone—whether it consists of normal or malformed tadpoles—is repeated in this generation. The change in nuclear properties is therefore fairly stable, and has actually been followed through quite a large number of generations.

In frogs the loss by the nuclei of their full capacity proceeds fairly rapidly after the blastula stage, and while the embryo is still at an early stage of differentiation there seem to be no nuclei left that can support the complete development of all types of tissue when tested in this way. However, in toads, of the genus Xenopus, the loss of capacity goes much more slowly. Even when the tissues are fully differentiated and functional, some of their nuclei, after transplantation, will allow a complete new animal to develop. This has been demonstrated, for instance, for a nucleus from a fully differentiated cell from the lining of the intestine. This shows that it is possible for a nucleus to control the production of cell-specific proteins while still retaining the genetic capacities required for the differentiation of other cell types.

We still do not understand the nature of the changes that have occurred in those nuclei that fail to support complete differentiation. Possibly all differentiation involves some degree of inactivation of the nonfunctioning genes, which becomes progressively more difficult to reverse so that these genes can operate again. Or possibly the alterations are in some more general characteristics, such as the nature of the nuclear envelope, and do not directly affect the genes themselves. The subject is one of the most important in the present phase of experimental embryology, and is being very actively studied.

CHAPTER

4

Regionalization and the Control of Gene Activity

THE PROBLEM OF HOW the various parts of an egg get directed into different paths of development, so that they produce the whole range of organs of the adult, has always been a central interest for embryologists. Fairly recently geneticists have also begun to ask themselves how the activities of the genes are controlled, so that some of them are switched on to produce their corresponding protein, while others are switched off. There are two types of situation in which the switching on or off of genes may occur. First, there is the regionalization problem; different genes may be switched on in different cells—for instance, the hemoglobin gene in a blood cell, the insulin gene in a pancreas cell, and so on. Second, in one and the same type of cell, different genes may be switched on at different times; for instance, a cell becomes definitely a blood cell, presumably by the switching on of some of its genes, a considerable time before it actually begins to produce hemoglobin, the gene for which is probably switched on some time later. The two types of switching may, of course, operate in exactly the same way. It is beginning to look, however, as though most of the studies of gene switching that have started from a genetic angle have actually been dealing with genes that come into play one after another during the gradual development of a cell, and that the switching which brings about the differentiation between different types of cells may involve another kind of mechanism (see page 87).

Another difficulty in interpreting data about when proteins are produced is that this may result from "translation" control at the ribosomes and not from "transcription" control of gene activity.

The Control of Single Genes in Bacteria

It will be logical to start with the genetic investigation of fairly simple systems, even though these studies were carried out more recently than most of the embryological work.

As we have seen, the product of a sequence of enzymes may inhibit the activity of some early enzyme in the series (end product inhibition, page 43). But there is another, and even more radical, influence that such substances may exert on the enzyme makeup of the cell. Many instances are known in which substances produced by enzymes influence not merely enzyme activity, but the actual production of the enzyme in question. For instance, arginine is produced by the series of steps shown in Figure 3·4, but if it is present in excess in the cell (for example, because it has been added to the culture medium), it suppresses the *formation* of the enzyme that brings about the ornithine-citrulline change. This is known as enzyme repression, and should be clearly distinguished from enzyme inhibition.

In some cases the presence in the medium of a particular molecule leads to the new production of an enzyme capable of metabolizing that molecule. For instance, if the sugar lactose is added to a culture of the bacterium *Escherichia coli* there is a very rapid production of an enzyme *beta galactosidase* which can break down lactose. This is enzyme induction, and an enzyme that can be produced in this way is said to be inducible. The molecules that act as inducers of it are mostly substances with which it can react, like lactose, although a few other substances, with molecules with some similarity to lactose but not reactive with the enzyme, will also act in this way. Reactions of this kind may be of great practical importance. For instance, when an antibiotic such as penicillin is present in the medium it can, in some strains of bacteria, induce the production of a penicillinase which destroys it, and thus reduces its efficiency.

Since bacteria can be grown in enormous numbers, it is practical with them, as it is not in most higher organs, to induce a lot of mutations with x-rays or ultraviolet and to look through these to find the particular mutations in which one is interested. In this way it has been possible to analyze in genetic terms the system that brings about enzyme induction or repression. It has been found that the inducing or repressing molecules do not react directly with the gene for the enzyme. Instead, they react first with a regulator substance which is present in the cytoplasm (or at least is not on the chromosomes, although it might be in nuclear sap). This regulator substance is produced by a particular gene, known as the *regulator gene* for that system. The enzyme whose production is controlled is produced by another gene, referred to as the "structural gene," because it controls the structure of the enzyme protein. In some cases the regulator substance controls the activities not of a single gene producing one enzyme, but of a small group of genes controlling several enzymes. The genes in the group lie side by side along the chromosome, and the activity of the whole group is controlled by one particular member. This controlling

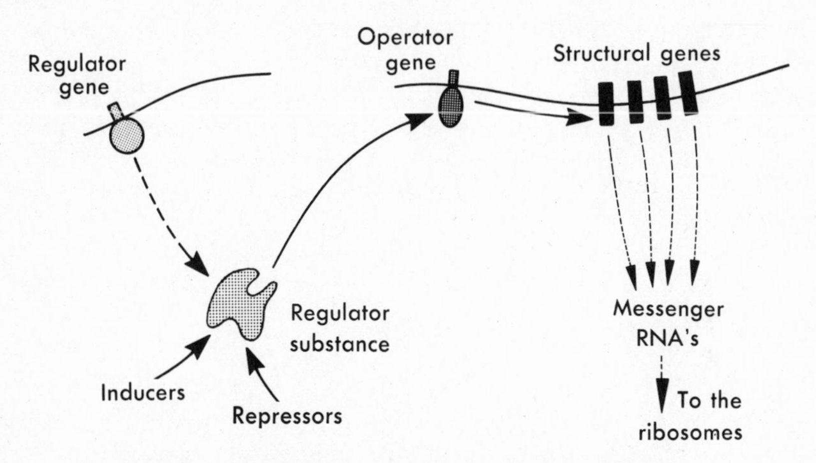

Figure 4·1. The regulation of gene activities in bacteria.

gene is known as the *operator,* and the whole group it controls is the *operon,* consisting of several enzyme-producing structural genes (Figure 4·1).

The property of the regulator substance is to react not only with the external inducer molecule but also with the operator gene. When one is dealing with an inducible enzyme, the regular substance is normally combined with the operator gene, and represses its activities so that no structural genes are active and none of the protein is made; but when the regulator substance is combined with the inducer molecule it can no longer react with the operator gene, and the whole operon then becomes active and produces its various enzymes. In the case of a repressible enzyme, the regulator substance is present but is not able to react with the operator gene until it is combined with the external repressing substance; when it is so combined, it reacts with the operator and represses its activities. It is noteworthy that in both cases the combination of the regulator substance with the operator gene represses the activity of the operator. The regulator substances are therefore sometimes called repressor substances.

If the regulator gene is put out of action by mutating to an inoperative form, there is no repressor substance produced, and the corresponding enzymes then become "constitutive"—that is, they appear in all cells, irrespective of the presence or absence of any external inducer substance.

The chemical nature of the regulator substances is still not entirely certain. Most of the evidence points to them being proteins. In fact they are probably allosteric proteins, with two active sites, one able to react with the operator, and one to react with the inducing or repressing external molecule (see page 43 and Figure 3·6). If one supposes that the properties of the operator site are altered according to whether the other site is or is not combined with an inducing or repressing molecule, then the whole system becomes easy to understand.

The Control of Single Genes in Higher Organisms

This system of inducible enzymes in bacteria provides one clear-cut mechanism by which gene activities can be controlled. It is quite likely that similar systems operate in more highly evolved organisms also. However, so far we do not know of any absolutely clear-cut example in a higher organism that can be analyzed so precisely. Moreover there are some reasons why one should be a little cautious in supposing that the control of gene activities in higher organisms is always carried out just in this way. For instance, the DNA in bacteria is normally combined with very little or no protein, whereas in higher organisms the DNA normally exists in the form of chromosomes which contain a large proportion of protein. Higher organism DNA might therefore be less easily controlled by allosteric protein regulator substances. Only time will tell how far this is so.

It is probably significant that in higher organisms, few if any examples are known of enzymes or other proteins becoming "constitutive" and appearing in every cell of the body. Such embryos would probably die at a fairly early stage; but so many young embryos have been looked at that if it ever happened that, for instance, the repressor of the hemoglobin gene was absent and this substance appeared in every cell, this should have been detected by now. The absence, or rarity, of such cases suggests that the control of single genes, by the mechanisms found in bacteria, is not the whole story, at least in the early stages of development. It seems rather likely that the control mechanisms that operate in early development act in some other way, to affect whole batteries of genes (see page 87), whereas, perhaps, control systems for single genes may come into play later. In any case, we have to remember that gene activity can be controlled not only by affecting transcription from DNA to RNA, as in the bacterial example just described, but also by affecting the translation of messenger RNA into protein (page 26).

We must now go on to consider examples of the control of gene activities in which the precise mechanisms operating are not so well understood. We may begin with an example in an organism that is somewhat more elaborate than a bacterium but is still rather simple—namely, the "slipper animalcule," the protozoan Paramecium. The character we are interested in is the appearance of one out of a number of possible protein substances on the surface of the cell. These are recognized by the fact that when they are injected into rabbits, the rabbit produces antibodies that react specifically with the particular antigens that have been administered.

Genetic analysis has shown that Paramecium contains a number of gene loci, at each of which there are several alleles controlling the production of a particular antigen. The important point that has emerged is that it is the "state of the cytoplasm" that decides which particular gene locus will be active, and thus which antigen will be formed. This is demonstrated by crossing experiments. When two paramecia mate they exchange nuclei, so that the nucleus from one strain comes into the cytoplasm of the other. The experimental results show that if a nucleus finds itself in this way in a new type of cytoplasm, then a new set of genes will be activated in it, and new antigens will be produced (Figure 4·2).

Unfortunately we still do not know what the "state of the cytoplasm" really amounts to. Presumably the "state" means that the cytoplasm contains some particular substances, and these substances may well be proteins, though this is not yet absolutely certain. Whatever the state is, it must be fairly labile, since it can be altered by changing the temperature, or by various alterations of the medium in which the cells are grown, and so on. It may well be that we are dealing with something like the changeable allosteric regulator substances found in bacteria. It would be particularly important if this could be definitely proved, since Paramecium has chromosomes containing a lot of protein, like those of higher organisms. However, at the present time the question of the nature of the state of the cytoplasm is still open.

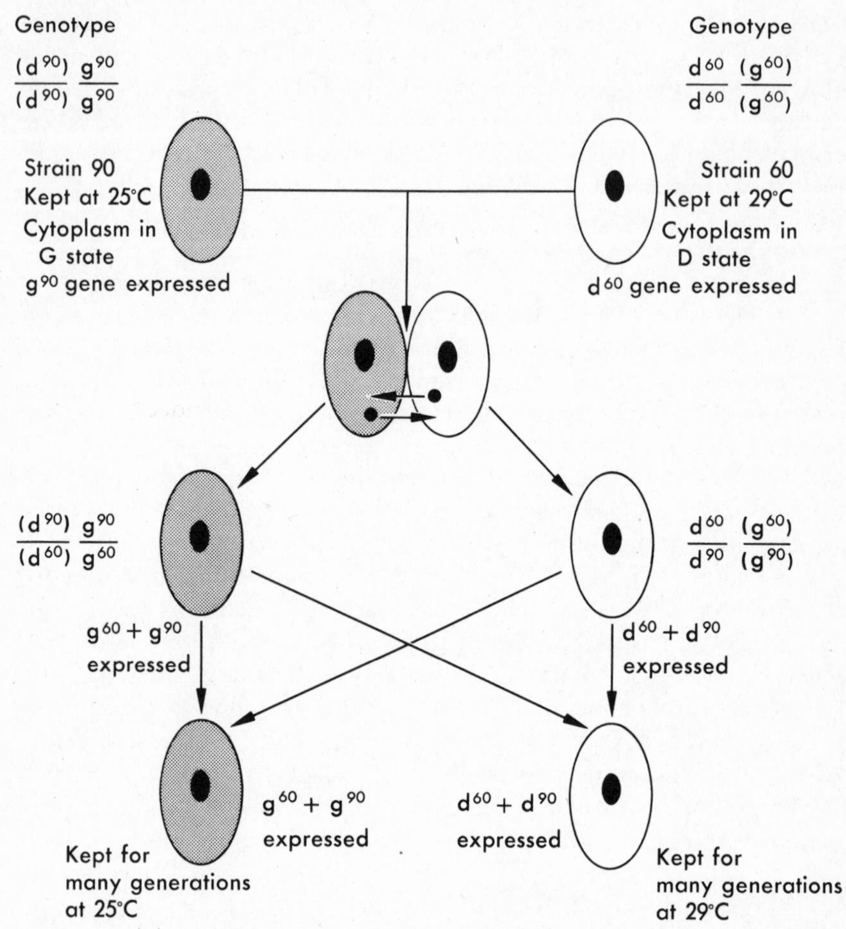

Figure 4·2. The inheritance of antigens in Paramecium. If paramecia are kept at 25° their cytoplasm gets into the G state, which causes activity by the genes at the G locus, producing a characteristic type of antigen. At 29° their cytoplasm is in the D state, and the genes at the D locus are active. At conjugation a haploid nucleus is passed from each individual into its partner, so that the two offspring are heterozygous for the genes from the two strains. Little or no cytoplasm is exchanged, and the cytoplasmic state changes only slowly in one direction or the other at temperatures between 25° and 29°. Thus at first in the daughters derived from the strain-90 parent the G alleles are active, including the g^{60} allele, which had not been expressed in the strain-60 parent. However, if these daughter cells are kept for many generations at 29° the cytoplasmic state changes from the G into the D state and the alleles at the D locus become activated and start producing their antigens. The daughter cells derived from the strain-60 parent show equivalent phenomena.

We can now go on to a case that is slightly more complicated again, since what is controlled it is not a single gene (or operon), but a sequence of genes acting one after the other. In this instance we are not quite certain what the genes are doing, but one can see by microscopic examination that they are doing something. In many species of flies, such as the fruit fly Drosophila, various midges, and so on, the cells in some organs become very large and contain enormous chromosomes. These chromosomes are produced because in the later stages of development the cells fail actually to divide, although the chromosomes in the nucleus go on dividing as usual. Thus the nucleus comes to contain many sets of chromosomes, and these may lie side by side in accurate register, forming very thick ropelike structures known as polytene (many stranded) chromosomes. When suitably stained these chromosomes show a pattern of dark and light crossbands. Now, at certain stages of development, in certain tissues, one can see a particular band swell up and in some cases actually see small globules of material being produced at it. Such swollen structures are known as puffs (Figure 4·3).

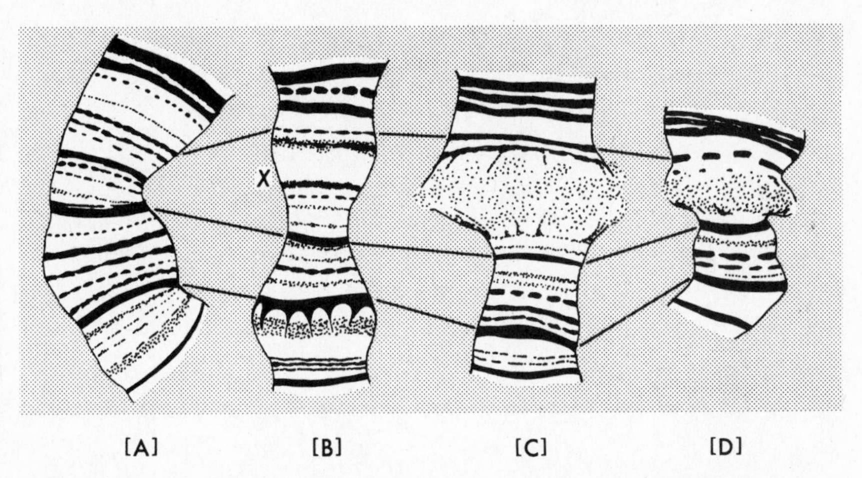

Figure 4·3. Four drawings of the same small section of the third chromosome in a midge *Chironomus*. A and B show this region in cells of the hindgut and the excretory (Malpighian) tubules in the larva; C and D show it in similar cells from the pupal stage. Note first that although the general pattern is the same in all cases, the precise degree of development of the various bands differs in the two types of tissue. Note also that at the place marked X, a slight puff occurs in the larval Malpighian tubules but not in the larval hindgut, while at the later pupal stage the same puff is more strongly expressed in both types of tissue.

Experiments with labeled compounds show that it is mainly RNA that is being produced at the puffs.

It is first important to notice that, in any given type of cell, puffs occur at definite chromosome bands at particular times. The cell type is characterized by a definite "puffing pattern," which affects both the places at which the puffs occur and the period in development when they occur. Different tissues have different characteristic puffing patterns. This is a very clear-cut demonstration that cellular differentiation involves the precise control of which genes will be active and at what times they will be active.

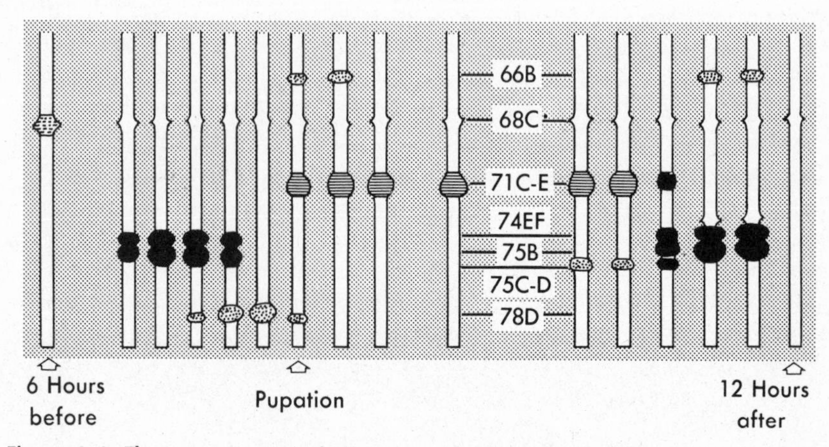

Figure 4·4. The appearance and disappearance of puffs ("puffing pattern") in the left arm of the third chromosome of *Drosophila melanogaster* during the last 6 hours of the larval period and the first 12 of the pupal period.

A great deal of work has been and still is being devoted to analyzing the control of chromosome puffing in these systems. In the first place it was necessary to work out precisely the puffing patterns of some definite tissues. This has now been done in a number of instances, particularly for the patterns that occur in the cells of the salivary gland of certain insects around the time that the larva changes into a pupa (Figure 4·4). In insects pupation is controlled by the antagonistic action of two hormones. One, the pupation hormone or ecdysone, tends to cause pupation; the other, the juvenile hormone, tends to make the animal remain a larva. It has been found in several species that if ecdysone is administered some time before pupation would normally occur, the pattern of puffs changes rapidly into that characteristic of the pupation stage. In fact the appearance of this puffing pattern is one of the very first changes that can be detected after the hormone has been given. On the other hand, if glands are removed from the larva and put into a neutral medium, and in particular if they are injured, the puffing pattern tends to change in the opposite way, toward the form characteristic of younger stages. This is one of the cases in which there seems to be some reversal of differentiation, but the reversal covers only a very short period in the final stages of the life history of the cells.

It is most unlikely that the hormones are acting directly on the DNA of the genes that exhibit puffing. The hormones are rather small molecules which could not be expected to recognize and react specifically with the particular types of DNA. Moreover the effects of ecdysone can be imitated by still simpler substances—for instance, by zinc chloride. Again, several other cases are known in which puffs can be induced at particular places in chromosomes by external agents of a very general kind, such as the alterations in balance of sodium and potassium. It seems almost certain, therefore, that in these systems the cells already contain some controlling or regulating substances that, on the one hand, are affected by agents like ecdysone or the juvenile hormone, and, on the other, react specifically with the particular genes that puff. Such regulator substances, which, like those in bacteria, travel to and interact with particular genes, have been spoken of as "genotropic substances." In the puffing situation we have no direct evidence of their nature, except that they probably are *not* the various compounds, like hormones, which have been used to induce the effects, but are more likely to be proteins, perhaps histones, attached to the various regions of the chromosomes.

There is another interesting piece of information about the control of puffing. As we have seen, the control normally affects not single genes but groups of genes which act in a sequence. The question can be asked, can the puffs occurring later in the sequence be activated without first activating the earlier ones? The problem has been tackled by destroying parts of the chromosomes, and thus putting out of action some of the genes that are normally involved in the whole series. It has been found that some of the later-appearing puffs do actually show up, even when the earlier ones have been suppressed in this way. Thus if there is normally a series of puffs appearing in the order *a, b, c, d, e, f,* we can show that when the sequence is induced, *f* will appear even when all the rest have been eliminated. This makes impossible the hypothesis that *a* acts to induce *b,* and *b* to induce *c,* and so on. It leads to the conclusion that the chromosomes must contain genotropic substances already attached to *a, b, c, d, e, f,* and that the attachment can be altered in such a way as to cause one gene to puff without any interaction with the others.

Genetic Switch Mechanisms

In studying puffing in salivary gland chromosomes, we are, of course, dealing only with genes that come into activity, one after the other, in the later stages of differentiation of cells that are already fully determined as salivary gland cells and nothing else. This is the second type of switching mentioned on page 59. It is really the first type, which causes the cell to become a salivary cell rather than, say, an intestinal cell, that is more important and more interesting. From the evidence we have just been considering, we might suspect that this would depend on some mechanism for attaching environmentally sensitive genotropic substances to the various genes. But we now have to look at some more of the available evidence.

The independence from one another of the successive steps in a sequence is not usually found when one studies genes that have important developmental effects. For instance, the action of the bithorax gene in Drosophila (page 22) switches the cells of the metathoracic segment into a whole new path of differentiation, that leading to wings. As a consequence of this switch, all the genes that are normally active in controlling wing development now become active in this segment. Unless the switch into wing development occurs, no way is known of making the other wing genes become active in these cells. This is a case, therefore, where the action of an early member of a sequence is necessary before the later members of the sequence can come into operation.

There are several other interesting points about these bithorax flies, which again emphasize how little we know about the real mechanisms of control of gene action. In the first place, the switching of the posterior segment of the thorax into wing development can be brought about not only by the main bithorax gene, which is at one particular locus on the chromosomes; exactly the same type of switch can be performed by the combined actions of a lot of genes each with relatively small effect and scattered about all over the three main chromosomes that Drosophila contains. One of these minor genes actually seems to operate by changing in some way the character of the egg laid by females containing it, and it is this change in egg character that finally leads to the abnormal switching of one part into a wing instead of into a balancer. Again, the switch can be produced, even in flies with a normal genotype, by the action of certain external agents (for example, ether vapor) on the early stages of embryonic development.

The conclusion seems to be that the switch can be operated by relatively unspecific agents, either external ones such as ether vapor, or general internal changes in the cells brought about by the action of many different genes. This is the same sort of situation we find with the puffing, which can be induced by something as unspecific as zinc chloride or sodium-potassium balance. Somewhere hidden in the whole system there must be specific genotropic substances, which go to and regulate the activities of the relevant genes. But we have not yet succeeded in getting hold of them. As we shall see, we shall be confronted with the same situation in the more purely embryological studies that will be described later.

POSITION EFFECTS

Before describing the work of the experimental embryologists, however, it is worth mentioning briefly one further type of gene control that has been studied by geneticists. Normally the position a gene occupies on the chromosome seems to have very little relation to the activities it exerts during development. For instance, there are genes acting on the wings of Drosophila, or on the eye pigments, in all the chromosomes, and there is only very slight evidence that in higher organisms the genes acting on the same cell, or the same set of developmental processes, are in any way grouped together, although this does occur in certain bacteria.

However, under certain special conditions the position of a gene in the chromosome may have an influence on its activity. In many organisms there are some regions of chromosomes that under the microscope look rather different from the rest, particularly because they have different affinities for dyes. These regions are referred to as "heterochromatin," in distinction to the normal parts of the chromosomes, which are euchromatin. (There are actually several kinds of heterochromatin, but that need not concern us here.) Now in several species that have been well analyzed genetically, particularly Drosophila and maize, it has been possible to cause chromosomes to break and the pieces to join together again in the wrong order. Then it is found that genes that have in this way been brought close to heterochromatin are quite often inactivated (Figure 4·5).

This is known as "position effect." It acts strictly along the chromosome. In most organisms where there are two similar sister chromosomes, if only one of the two is broken and rejoined in this way, inactivation operates on the genes in the broken chromosome but has no effect on the similar genes in the unbroken one. In this the action is similar to that of the operator gene in bacteria which controls the set of structural genes in the operon connected with it, but has no effect on similar genes in other chromosomes.

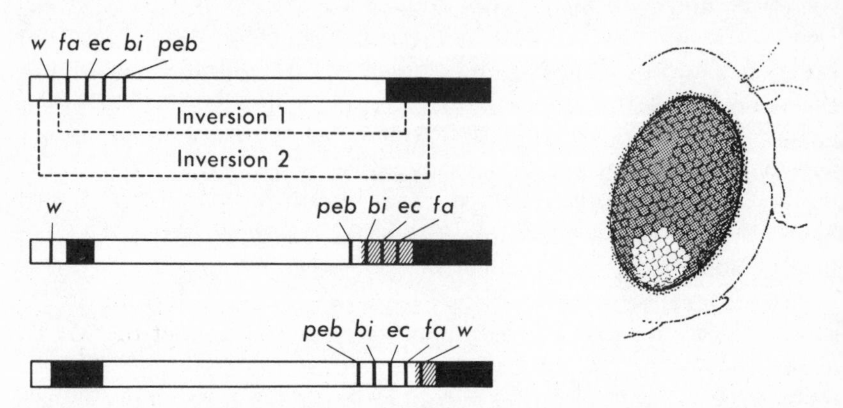

Figure 4·5. Position effect. The normal X chromosome of Drosophila is shown in diagrammatic form at the top. There is a large block of heterochromatin (black) at the right end of the chromosome, and the diagram indicates a number of genes (*w, fa, ec, bi, peb*) located toward the left end. Two lower diagrams show two different inversions in which a section of the chromosome has been broken out and replaced in the wrong order. In Inversion 1, the heterochromatin at the right end causes a position effect spreading through the genes *fa, ec,* and *bi* but not as far as *peb*. In Inversion 2 there is a position effect on *w* but not on *fa*.

The drawing on the right shows the appearance of a "variegated" eye in Drosophila, in which the *w* gene has been inactivated by a position effect, in some cells, giving rise to a patch of white ommatidia in the otherwise red eye.

However, the position effect in higher organisms acts along the chromosomes for far greater distances than the operator effects in bacteria. It can cause inactivation of large sections of chromosome, containing perhaps several hundred genes. Its mechanism is very obscure, though there are several theories; but it is not impossible—and some people strongly support the suggestion—that actions of this kind play an important part in controlling normal development.

The Amphibian Egg

It is now time to turn to the studies on switch mechanisms that have been made by embryological rather than genetic methods.

The most thorough and far-reaching studies have been carried out in amphibia—frogs and, particularly, newts and salamanders. The eggs of these animals are fairly large, about two millimeters in diameter. They contain a fair amount of yolk in the form of granules scattered through the cytoplasm, and this enables them to live in dilute salt solutions, using their yolk as a source of energy, until the embryo develops into a complicated tadpole able to feed for itself. Even small groups of cells, cut out from an embryo and isolated in salt solution, will continue to live and develop. Moreover, the embryos are very good at healing wounds, and this makes it possible to graft small pieces taken from one place into some other location, either in the same or in a different embryo. The eggs are, therefore, very suitable for experimental manipulation, and they have been as much the favorite objects of embryologists as the fruit fly Drosophila was for so long the favorite of geneticists.

The essential structure of the egg at the time of fertilization is simple. The yolk platelets, although scattered throughout the whole, are more concentrated at the lower, vegetative, end, and the nucleus tends to lie toward the other, animal, pole, which is also more deeply pigmented in the surface layer. Soon after fertilization a further regional difference puts in an appearance. One can detect a special cytoplasmic region, lying slightly below the equator of the egg and concentrated on one side of the main axis. This side will eventually develop into the structures of the backbone of the animal, and all through early development the region formed by this special cytoplasm plays an extremely important role.

The first question to be asked, therefore, is how does this region of cytoplasm—often spoken of as "the gray crescent," which describes its appearance in the eggs of some species—come to be located on one particular side of the egg? The localization is quite a complicated process, depending on the interaction of several factors. For one thing, the crescent always appears just above the main concentration of yolk at the vegetative pole. If the egg is turned upside down and held that way, so that the yolk falls to the bottom of it in its new position, then the crescent will form above this displaced mass (Figure 4·6).

This factor, however, is only sufficient to locate the crescent somewhere just below the equator, and does not specify on which side of the egg it will appear. Experiments have shown that two factors are involved in this. One is some sort of built-in structure, characteristic of the egg at the time it is laid. This may be a feature of the outer surface, or cortex, of the egg, but it is not fully understood. Its effect is that, from the time of laying, one side of the egg has a certain tendency to be the position at which the crescent will form and the dorsal organs develop. However, this tendency is not very firmly fixed, and can be overcome. For instance, if the fertilizing sperm is led into an egg along a thread and therefore forced to penetrate it at the point where the thread touches the egg surface, then it is often found that the crescent appears at the side of the egg opposie the point of penetration, even though that may not be the side predisposed for it.

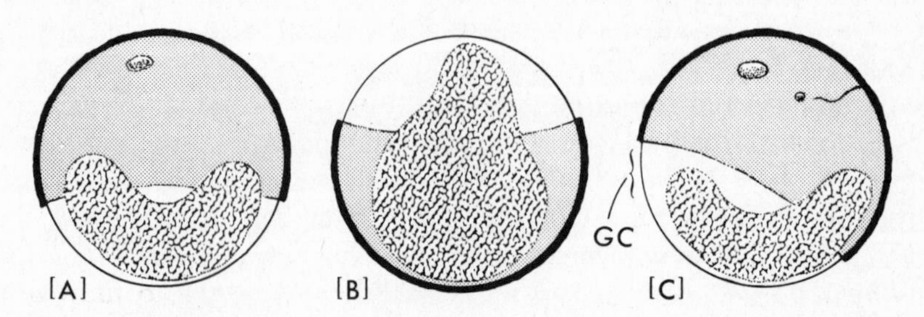

Figure 4·6. Formation of the gray crescent. A: A section through a frog egg before fertilization. The upper two-thirds of the egg is covered by a heavily pigmented layer, and the heaviest yolk forms a rather cup-shaped mass at the lower vegetative end. When a fertilized egg is held upside down, the yolk gradually pours down from the upper region to the lower (**B**); and the gray crescent, and later the blastopore, will be formed somewhere just above this—that is, within the pigmented layer. **C:** Normal fertilization. The sperm has entered in the upper right and is moving off toward the egg nucleus. The whole pigmented cap is rotated toward the point of sperm penetration. It is the region on the other side of the egg, from which the pigmented coat has moved away, that becomes the gray crescent (GC).

The importance of the crescent for future development was proved many years ago. If a newt's egg is pinched in two by a loop of thread, both halves may produce a complete normal adult (page 55). However, a portion of an egg will only develop fully if it contains a sufficient quantity of the crescent. If the plane of the constriction happens to put the whole crescent in one half, leaving the other half without any, the second half may undergo cell division if it contains a nucleus, but never produces any of the characteristic adult tissues; its cells remain embryonic and without any special features. It is, therefore, the cytoplasm of the crescent that first switches on the gene activities that control the synthesis of the proteins characteristic of adult cell types. Cells lacking the crescent material can, presumably, synthesize the proteins required for the mitotic spindles used at cell division, but they do not seem able to synthesize anything else.

With modern methods we have recently been able to see signs

of the switching on of gene activity, beginning quite early in development. After the usual period of cleavage into a large number of cells, the amphibian egg forms a hollow blastula in which the layer of animal cells, with little yolk, is much thinner than the mass of vegetative cells, which are very yolky. It then starts its process of gastrulation, by which the hollow ball is converted into a three-layered embryo (see page 3). In these eggs, gastrulation involves part of the upper animal region of the egg being folded into the interior through a fairly narrow hole, which pushes from the outside inward, making a finger-shaped cavity, which is called the primitive gut and eventually turns into the intestine. This hole, known as the blastopore, appears just at the bottom of the crescent. If an egg at this stage is offered the raw materials of proteins or nucleic acids—amino acids or nucleotides—labeled with radioactive isotopes, most of the cells absorb very little of them, which is evidence that little synthesis is going on. However, just in the cells derived from the crescent, which are now beginning to move into the blastopore, there is a rapid uptake of these substances, and they become built into proteins and nucleic acids.

The newly synthesized materials of both these types are at first located mainly in the cell nucleus. In fact we can locate them more precisely, in the nucleolus inside the nucleus. This organelle is lacking in the very early embryonic cells of most amphibians, and begins to put in an appearance in the blastopore cells about the time gastrulation begins. The exact function of the nucleolus of these cells is still somewhat uncertain, but the evidence suggests it is concerned with the synthesis of the machinery that will be required for protein synthesis, in particular the synthesis of the soluble RNA and of the ribosome particles to which messenger RNA will later become attached. It is, of course, reasonable to assume that the first genes that it would be necessary to switch would be those controlling the synthesis of ribosomes, which are an essential part of the machinery which other genes can use later to produce their specific proteins.

The crescent material makes up only a small fraction of the whole egg, perhaps a tenth of it. How do the genes get switched on in other regions? One of the main reasons why the amphibian egg has been so fascinating to embryologists is that we can prove that the switching in other parts of the egg is strongly affected by influences that originate within the crescent region and then move out from it.

The original demonstrations of this effect were made some forty years ago, long before anyone seriously tried to interpret development in genetic terms. The experiments used straightforward embryological techniques, of cutting out one part of an egg and grafting it on some other egg at a different place, or simply excising a portion of the egg and isolating it in a salt solution.

If any small fragment of the animal part of the gastrula, lying above the crescent, is cut out and isolated, it fails to develop into any of the more specialized adult cell types, and forms instead only a rather rudimentary type of skinlike tissue. Probably this involves the operation of some genes, but surely not of very many. Now in normal development the cells in the blastopore region are folded into the interior of the egg and come to lie underneath a large part of the animal half. It is just the part of the exterior that becomes underlain that develops into the main ectodermal organs of the dorsal axis or backbone—namely, the brain and neural tube. Meanwhile the cells from the blastopore region continue their own development, turning into the muscles, kidneys, and so on. They will, in fact, do this when isolated as small groups in salt solution. It certainly looks as though the development of the brain and nervous system might be influenced by something coming from the underlying cells of the blastopore as they develop into the mesodermal organs.

A definite proof of this can be made by putting together in a salt solution two fragments, one taken from the animal pole and the other from the crescent region. In these circumstances the animal pole fragment, which if isolated would develop only into a simple type of skin, is now found to develop into nerve cells characteristic of the brain and neural system. Or one can take a piece of the crescent region from one embryo and graft it into another so that it comes to underlie a part that would normally develop into the skin; it is then found that these "prospective" skin cells now develop into a brain or other part of the nervous system (Figure 4·7).

The process by which one part of an embryo, in this case the crescent region, influences some neighboring part, such as the prospective skin cells, making that part develop into an organ which it would not otherwise have done, is spoken of as "embryonic induction." It is a very common process in embryonic development. In vertebrates such as newts, birds, and mammals, very many types of induction have been described. For instance, shortly after the crescent cells have induced the formation of the brain and nervous system, about the time of gastrulation, these organs begin to induce other things in their turn. The very front tip of the brain induces the formation of the nose organs; slightly behind this, two outgrowths from the brain, which later develop into the eyes, induce the overlying skin to form the lenses; still further posteriorly the hindbrain induces the ears; and so on. Similar processes have also been found in the embryos of various invertebrate groups, but there is no space to describe these here.

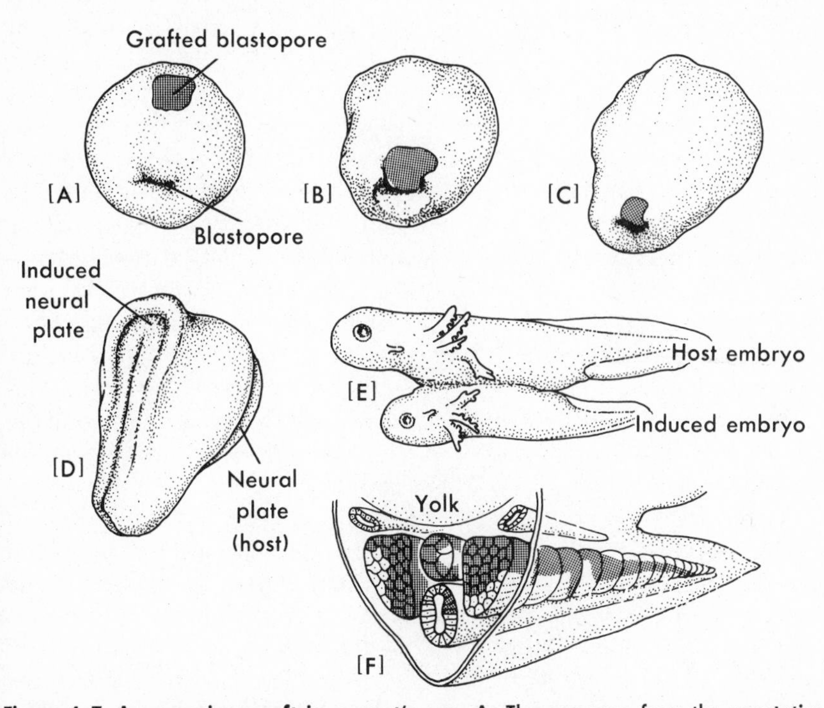

Figure 4·7. An organizer graft in a newt's egg. A: The egg seen from the vegetative pole. Its own blastopore is lying at the lower side of the drawing, while at the other side there has been grafted a fragment from the blastopore region of another egg (which was stained with a vital dye to make it more visible). In **B** and **C** this grafted material moves into the interior of the egg just as does the tissue around the host blastopore. In **D** one can see at the lower side the edge of the neural plate (that is, neural fold) of the host embryo, and on the upper side a second neural plate formed in connection with the graft. (These four figures are taken from a cinema film.) **E:** A diagrammatic drawing of a similar embryo at a later stage. In **F** we have a section and perspective drawing of part of the yolk of the host embryo and the structure of the secondary embryo. Dark cells are derived from the graft; light cells are host material that has been induced to undergo these types of differentiation.

Nearly all the experiments that have been carried out up to date on embryonic induction have used small fragments of embryonic tissue, containing perhaps a hundred or more cells. It is only in the last few years that work has been begun in which individual cells have been studied. In many embryos it is possible to disaggregate the tissues, during early stages at least, and thus to obtain single cells which can be isolated or combined in various ways. It is general experience that single cells which have been isolated from tissues that normally contain many hundreds of cells will not differentiate. There is a minimum number—different for different species and stages and types of tissue—that must be put fairly close together before it is possible for differentiation to go forward. This minimum number is larger if the cultures have a greater volume, lesser if it has a smaller, which suggests that the isolated cells tend to lose some essential components by diffusion into the medium. Processes of induction can also be observed. For instance, separated ectoderm cells from the amphibian gastrula do not develop into nerve cells unless they come into contact, or near contact, with cells from the mesoderm. One very active subject of debate at the present time is whether the substances presumed to be acting during induction are the same as those whose loss into the medium by diffusion prevents further differentiation. There are hints, at least, that both types of substances may be ribonucleoproteins, but there is not yet much firm evidence about them.

At present our insight into these processes is still based mainly on experiments with tissue masses—that is, groups of cells—rather than with single cells.

Induction processes as they occur in living embryos are quite complicated and involve several different types of reaction. Their study has unfortunately been somewhat bedeviled by the rather unfortunate terminology introduced by the original German workers on the subject. They used words which, when translated into English, or American, seem to some biologists to have a rather mystical flavor. But this is really beside the point. The facts, though complicated, are quite definite facts, and deserve a proper scientific explanation.

One of the main complexities is this. In a living embryo the crescent cells do not merely switch the neighboring cells into a new line of synthesis so that they produce the proteins characteristic of nerve cells. The induction gives rise to a well-organized brain and nervous system, with an elaborate morphological structure and pattern (Figure 4·7). This, of course, involves a much higher level of complexity or biological organization than a mere collection of cells containing specific nerve proteins. The original German words seem to imply that induction always involves these complex levels of organization, since the word chosen to refer to what we have called the crescent cells was "the organization center" or, for short, "the organizer." Now this really confuses two issues. It is perfectly possible to switch a mass of embryonic cells, from becoming a disorderly group of skin cells into becoming an equally disorderly collection of nerve cells, with no or minimal organization (Figure 4·8). This is, in some sense, "an induction." But something that brings this about is scarcely entitled to be called an organizer. It is better to refer to it instead as an "evocator." When

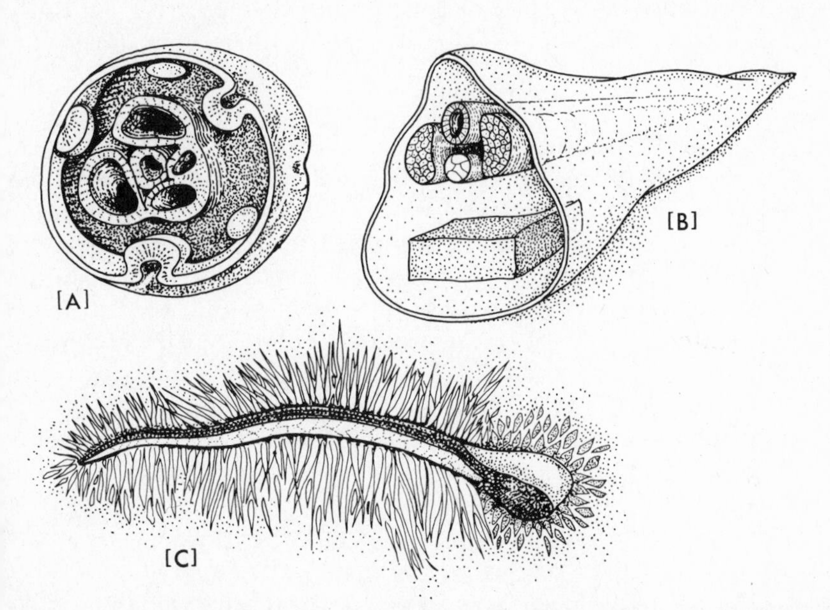

Figure 4·8. Individuation in tissue explants from newt's eggs. A: A fragment of gastrula ectoderm that has been cultured in an evocating substrate and has developed into a very disorderly mass of neural tissue covered by a thin layer of skin in which some nasal placodes have appeared; there is a minimum of individuation. **B:** A sheet of gastrula ectoderm was wrapped round a fragment of dead adult liver, which has evocated in it a well-formed embryonic axis (neural tube, notochord, and somites). Since the dead liver can hardly have played a part in specifying the details of this pattern, the mass of induced tissue must have individuated itself. **C:** A fragment from the blastopore region of a gastrula has been cultured and has developed into a number of tissues (dark neural tube, light notochord, muscle cells, head mesenchyme) showing some orderliness in arrangement, which must again be due to self-individuation.

morphological organization occurs as well, as it often does, then we are obviously dealing with something more, and we require another word to refer to it. Since "organization" has already been used in a loose sense to refer to the whole process, it is better to use for this purpose the word "individuation." It is still reasonable to go on using the expression "embryonic induction" when we want to refer to the whole process, without specifying precisely any particular aspect of it.

There is another important aspect to induction for which we also require a word. The induction of a particular organ can only be carried out on the cells from a particular part of an embryo at a particular stage in their development. For instance, the cells of an early amphibian embryo do not begin to respond to the evocators of nervous tissue until about the time of gastrulation, and they lose this responsiveness again fairly soon after gastrulation ends. The word "competence" is used to describe their state during the

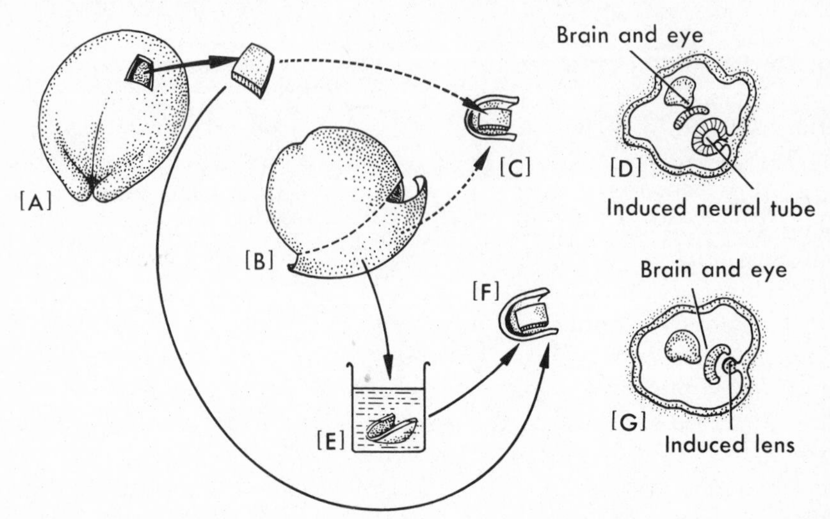

Figure 4·9. Competence. B: An early newt gastrula seen from above with the blastopore just out of sight at top left. The ectodermal region above the dotted line is removed and its competence tested by wrapping it round a fragment taken from the brain—eye region of an open neural plate stage embryo (**A**) which is capable of induction. If this inducer is combined with the gastrula ectoderm immediately after the latter is isolated (**C**) the inducer develops into brain and eye, and induces from the ectoderm part of the neural tube (**D**). If, however, the gastrula ectoderm is kept for 36 hours in salt solution (**E**) before the inducer is added to it (**F**), its competence has changed, and now in response to the same inducer it forms a lens (**G**).

period when they can respond; or we can speak of them at that time as "competent with respect to neural induction." A little later they will become competent with respect to other types of induction, for instance that of a lens. Interpreted in genetic terms this must mean that there is only a certain period during which the particular genes for these types of tissues are susceptible to being switched on or off (Figure 4·9).

One of the important general questions about development is the nature of this susceptibility to switching. Are the genes in the very early embryonic cells perhaps combined with something else, which puts them out of reach of the usual regulator substances? Does this something have to be removed before the normal switch mechanisms can come into operation? Unfortunately we still know hardly anything about this, and it is a problem that it has not yet been possible to tackle with the more modern molecular biological methods of approach.

The Early Chick Embryo

Armed with the three words *evocation, individuation,* and *competence,* we can describe the whole complicated range of phenomena that we find in various cases of induction in normal embryos.

We will therefore use them to describe the phenomena of regionalization in another type of vertebrate—the chick embryo. This has the advantage that hens' eggs are very easily obtained for study in class, but it has the disadvantage that the early development of birds is somewhat complicated.

The complications are caused by the presence in the egg of enormous stores of yolk. The actual egg cell of the bird is the yellow part conventionally referred to as the yolk. All the rest—such as the membrane around the yolk ("vitelline" membrane), the albumen, shell membranes, and the shell itself—are outside the egg cell proper, and have been laid down around it as it is passed down through the genital tract of the female. Within the "yolk" or egg cell, the living cytoplasm forms a very small patch near the surface at one point, and it is here that the egg nucleus lies. The fertilization takes place within the body of the hen not long before the egg is laid. When the fertilized egg cell begins to cleave, the planes separating the new cells do not cut right through the huge mass of yolky material, but simply divide off small portions of the patch of living cytoplasm. The cleavage, therefore, does not produce a hollow blastula of the kind seen in the frog or newt, but instead finishes up with a small, circular, flat plate of cells floating on the surface of a sphere of undivided yolk (Figure 4·10).

This circular plate of cells is known as the blastoderm. It is several cells thick. It is from this fairly thick circular plate that the three fundamental layers of ectoderm, mesoderm, and endoderm have to be produced. In the chick the folding processes of gastrulation are rather long drawn out, and take place in two rather distinct phases; in the first the endoderm is formed, and in the second the remainder of the blastula separates into ectoderm and mesoderm.

Endoderm formation starts at one side of the circular blastoderm, which will eventually be the posterior end of the embryo. Most of the endoderm is formed simply from the lower cells in the blastoderm, which gradually separate off the upper cells, but there may also be some movement of upper cells downward into the depths to join them (Figure 4·10). The process starts at the posterior side of the blastoderm and gradually moves toward the anterior. During the whole process the blastoderm is rapidly growing. Its lower cells, particularly those around the circumference, are taking in yolk granules, digesting them, and increasing the amount of living cytoplasm. Very soon these peripheral cells become heavily charged with yolk, so that they become quite opaque and form a

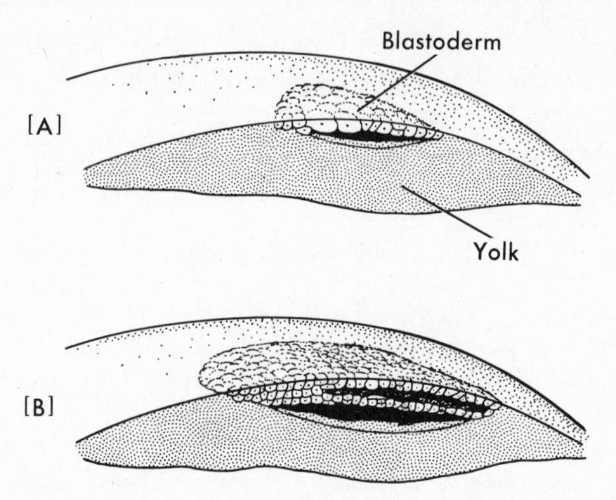

Figure 4·10. Chick cleavage. A: A section through an early cleavage stage of the chick embryo. B: A further stage, in which the lower cells are becoming separated from the upper ones to form the endoderm.

ring around the embryo referred to as the "area opaca." The more central parts of the blastoderm are not so active in yolk assimilation and the cells are more transparent, so that this part is known as the "area pellucida."

At this stage the blastoderm has a great capacity for individuation. If it is cut in half, or even into much smaller fragments, every fragment will proceed to form a complete embryo. In the reorganization of the fragments as they individuate themselves into complete organisms, it is the posterior end of the blastoderm, where endoderm formation began, that takes the lead. For instance, if the cut separates an anterior half from a posterior half, the embryo in the posterior half always develops in the original direction, whereas in the anterior half its polarity may be reversed. In fact, the posterior region has the properties of an inducer. If, shortly after the endoderm has become distinct, it is separated from the upper layer and rotated so that it now lies head to tail in comparison with its original direction, the posterior part of it induces a new embryo in the upper layer, running in the reverse direction to that of the original embryo.

The first sign of the appearance of an embryo in the upper layer is the formation of a thickened elongated region, named the primitive streak. This structure corresponds in some sense to the blastopore seen in embryos in which the blastula is a hollow sphere. It is,

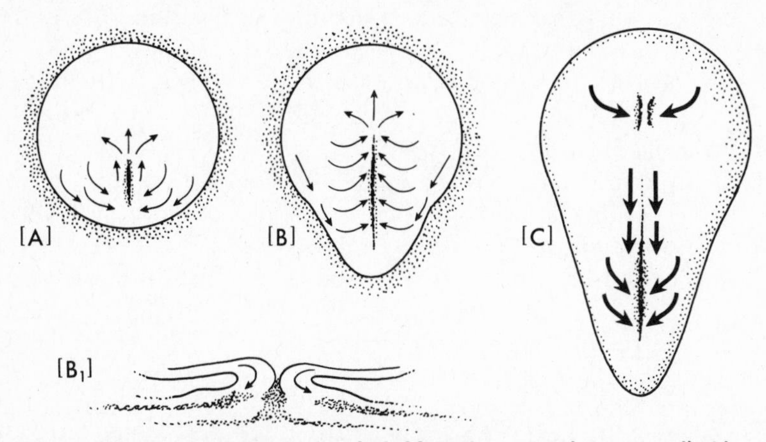

Figure 4·11. Tissue movements in the chick blastoderm. A: The *area pellucida* soon after the primitive streak appears. Material is moving in toward the streak at the posterior, and then forward along it. The combination of these two movements causes the circular blastoderm to be drawn out into a pear-shaped area shown in drawing **B;** material is still moving in from the sides toward the streak and forward along it, and at the same time it turns down through the streak to become mesoderm layer, as shown in the diagrammatic cross section in figure B_1. By the stage shown in **C,** the neural groove is beginning to appear in the anterior end. The streak is now rapidly shortening, and there is a powerful movement backward along it.

for instance, the region at which the mesoderm is formed and separated from the ectoderm. However, it is also the center of very extensive movements of growth and extension, which causes the chick embryo to appear as an extremely elongated structure. This lengthening of the main axis of the embryo involves not merely growth but also streaming movements by which parts of the blastoderm change their relative positions.

In the early stages the streaming takes place from the posterior toward the anterior (Figure 4·11). This forward movement along the primitive streak continues until the area pellucida is drawn out into quite a thin pear-shaped area. At this time the anterior tip of the streak becomes somewhat thickened, forming a little knob referred to as Hensen's node. The forward streaming is soon succeeded by a backward movement. This starts at the anterior end of the streak, around Hensen's node, and if marks are now placed in this region they are found to move backward along the streak.

These streamings, forward and then backward, are superimposed on another movement which is in some ways even more important. The cells lying on each side of the streak move from the sides toward the middle, forming two streams, which meet head-on in the streak, where they turn downward into the depths, curve round, and come out again at a lower level between the uppermost layer of cells and the endoderm, which is already in place below (Figure 4·11). This movement obviously gives rise to an intermediate middle layer, the mesoderm.

Soon after the mesoderm reaches its location between the other two layers, some of the definitive organs of the embryo put in an appearance (Figure 4·12). The central region of the ectoderm becomes thicker, folds up first into a groove and then into a tube, and begins to develop into the brain and spinal cord. In the middle layer, a central strand becomes separated off as the notochord, and on each side of this the sheet of tissue becomes separated into more or less cuboidal blocks, known as the somites, out of which the vertebrae and many of the muscles of the trunk will later develop. Underneath the head region the endoderm folds forward in a pocket which is the beginning of the intestine, and on each side of this some of the mesoderm accumulates to form the heart.

It is at this stage, therefore, that the various regions definitely begin on different paths of differentiation. The switching on of these various types of differentiation involves many processes of induction; and again one can distinguish the two aspects of induction—evocation and individuation. For instance, if a piece of the primitive streak of one embryo is grafted into another so that it lies under ectoderm that would normally form part of the skin, it performs an evocation so that this ectoderm now develops into nervous tissue (Figure 4·13). Similarly, just as in the amphibia, the outgrowth from the brain that gives rise to the retina of the eye evokes the formation of a lens from the ectoderm with which it comes in contact. The hindbrain evokes the formation of the ears, and so on. Each of these processes can only take place during a certain period of development, which is limited to the stage at which the reacting materials are competent.

Phenomena of individuation are also very obvious. When a piece

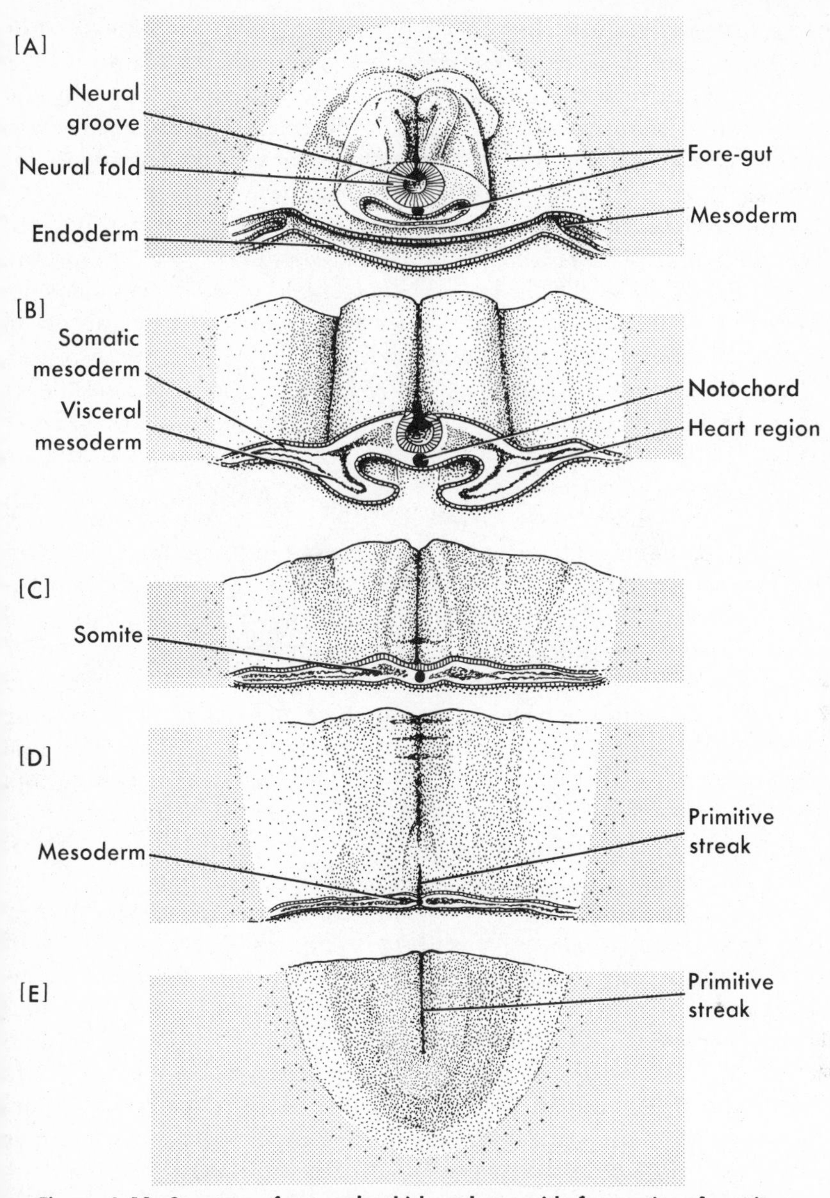

Figure 4·12. Structure of an early chick embryo with four pairs of somites.

of the primitive streak is grafted under lateral ectoderm, and evokes this to form some new structure, this often becomes organized to form a morphologically recognizable part of an embryo, such as a head. If the induced structure lies near the main embryo there is often a mutual influence between them; any induced structure lying near the head of the host embryo tends to be a head. If the two structures lie very close they may become partially or completely fused to form more or less unified structures. Again, if any part of the primitive streak is isolated, during its development it self-individuates itself into some more or less normal region of the embryonic axis, and in doing so nearly always forms rather more of an embryo than would have been expected.

We still have little precise knowledge about the processes going on during such individuation. There clearly must be two aspects of them. On the one hand, there must be a separation of different regions; for instance, a portion of the primitive streak will separate

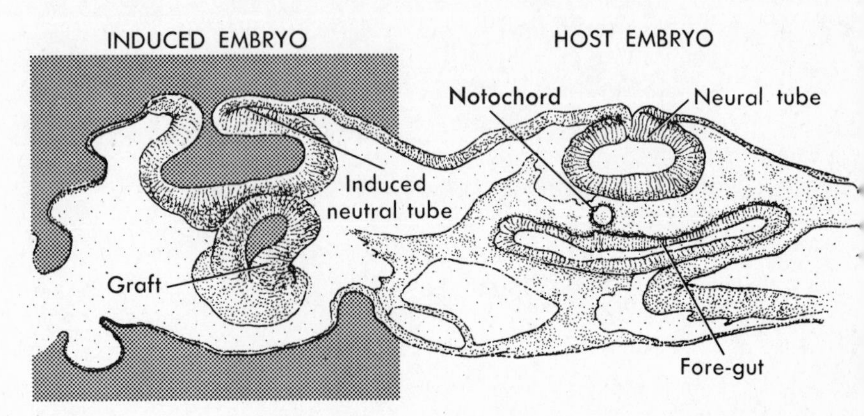

Figure 4·13. An induction in the chick embryo. The drawing shows a section in which the main host embryo lies on the right with the neural tube above the notochord, under which is the foregut. When this embryo was in the primitive streak stage a fragment of primitive streak from another embryo had been planted under the region that lies on the left of the section. The grafted fragment has developed into neural tissues and some mesoderm, and the ectoderm lying above it has been induced to form a secondary neural tube.

into a piece of neural tissue, a strand of notochord, and two rows of somites. This seems to involve some sort of autonomous sorting out of different characteristics. At the same time it is clear that the different regions also influence one another: as is seen when the head region of the host embryo influences the type of development of an induction lying near it.

We can, so far, explain these phenomena only in a very general way. It seems that at an early stage some important characteristics of the cells are distributed in a number of gradients; for instance, the tendency to form notochord is strongest in the midline and falls off on either side, and there is also clearly a strong anterior-posterior gradient in the tendency to develop into the anterior structures included in the head. We have to suppose that the gradients of two regions put in contact can influence one another, and also that the characteristics which are originally distributed in continuous gradients gradually become sorted out into distinct regions, rather as cream slowly separates as a distinct layer on the top of a bottle of milk. Unfortunately, we still have no precise notion of the chemical nature of the "important characteristics of the cells" distributed in these gradients.

There is, of course, another aspect of the individuation—namely, the folding and bending of the tissues into the precise shapes of the brain, heart, and so on. These are the processes of morphogenesis which we shall discuss in the last chapter.

Physicochemical Nature of the Switch Mechanisms

Several embryonic induction processes or switch mechanisms have been studied from a physicochemical point of view. Although it seems that in no case have we yet identified the most crucially important substances controlling the switch, we have by now a good deal of information about the general nature of the mechanisms involved.

One of the first and most thoroughly studied switch mechanisms is that by which the mesoderm in the amphibian egg triggers off the ectoderm lying above it to develop in the direction of neural tissue. In the normal undisturbed egg it is only the blastopore cells which are folded inward to form the mesoderm that are capable of performing this induction. However, it was soon discovered that neural induction can be carried out by many tissues, both alive and dead, from older embryos or adult animals.

The first reaction of biologists to this information was to suppose that this would make it easy to extract from these adult tissues, which can be obtained in large quantity, the *active inducing substance*, which would be difficult to purify if one had to start with the very small living blastopore region. Several very active inducing substances were in fact extracted from adult tissues by various groups of workers. However, different laboratories came up with different active substances, and it fairly soon became apparent that the problem had been seen in too simple a manner.

The clue lay in the observation that the parts of the gastrula that are normally inactive acquire the power of inducing after they have been killed. This certainly suggests that the active inducing substance is already present within the cells, but for some reason is not effective while those cells are alive. In the blastopore region, where the folding of the mesoderm into the interior of the egg is proceeding, the cellular metabolism is different from that in the remainder of the egg—for instance, there is a rapid utilization of glycogen and, as we have seen, a rapid synthesis of new proteins and nucleic acid, particularly in the nucleoli. It seemed reasonable to suppose that it was something to do with this special metabolism that caused the inducing substance in the cells to become active. In fact, it was found that various treatments that affect cell metabolism but do not kill the cells are able to bring the normally inactive parts of the gastrula into a state of inductive activity.

Now these treatments (such as the action of certain dyes that stimulate oxidation, mild heat shocks, strong osmotic pressures, or abnormal pH) are much too unspecific to act directly on the activities of the particular genes controlling the synthesis of nerve proteins. We must in fact be dealing with a situation that has many similarities with that which has been discovered more recently in induced enzyme synthesis in bacteria. There, as we have seen, the cells contain regulator substances which can, on the one hand, act specifically to repress or derepress particular genes, while, on the other hand, their ability to do this is affected by their interaction with relatively unspecific inducer molecules in the medium. In embryonic induction the cells must also contain some regulator substances capable of specifically activating or derepressing certain genes; and again the effectiveness of these regulator substances must be altered by less specific changes in the metabolism of the cells, which can be brought about in many different ways. In the early studies on amphibian neural induction, the gene-controlling or "genotropic" regulating substance was referred to as the "masked evocator," and it was supposed that this was without effect until some change in cellular metabolism, such as that which occurs at the blastopore region, brought it into play (Figure 4·14).

We know even less about the chemical nature of the masked evocator regulator substance in embryonic cells than we do about the regulator substances in bacterial enzyme induction. In the latter, as we have seen, the regulator may probably be an allosteric protein with two active sites in the molecule, one specific for a particular gene and the other capable of acting with the less specific inducer molecules. In embryonic cells the regulator substances capable of acting specifically on particular genes may also be proteins. However, we are still very far from having identified them; and one must remember that the situation in the cells of the higher organisms is certainly much more complicated than that in the simple cells of bacteria. It is worth noticing what some of these complexities are. In the first place, in higher organisms such as amphibians the DNA of the genes normally exists in combination with protein. The activity of the DNA therefore cannot be changed merely by the attachment or removal of protein; the only possible mechanism of this sort would be one that involves a change in the kind of protein that is attached. Again, as we have seen, embryonic cells become competent to react to inducing substances only at particular times. It is still quite uncertain how this should be inter-

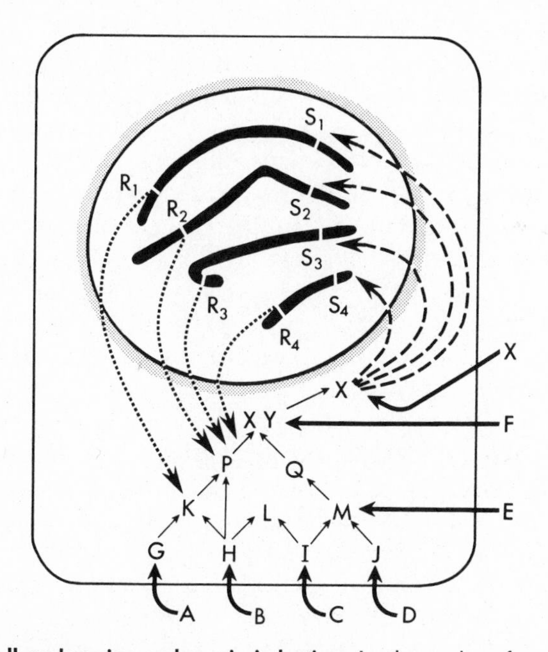

Figure 4·14. Cell undergoing embryonic induction. In the nucleus four chromosomes are shown (in haploid condition for simplicity) which contain four structural genes, S_1 to S_4, which control the formation of the proteins involved in some particular course of differentiation—say, into neural tissue. The whole of this battery of genes is switched on (or derepressed) by a genotropic substance X, which is the true evocator. In the cell before induction this substance is inactivated, or masked, in the form XY, which is itself involved in the elaborate metabolic fluxes going on in the cytoplasm. The substances concerned in these metabolic changes (G, H, I, K, L, P, Q, and so on) are formed under the control of another set of genes, R_1 to R_4, which act as regulator genes (cf. the maternally acting genes in Limnea, Figure 2·2). The condition of this whole metabolic system defines the "cytoplasmic state" in the sense used about Paramecium (see Figure 4·2). Many external influences (A to F) impinging on this metabolic system may cause the release or activation of X. All such influences are "indirect evocators." The most important problems we are faced with are (1) to identify X itself; (2) to discover how X switches on the whole battery of genes S_1 to S_4; (3) to discover what brings the cell into the competent state shown in the diagram: is this due to activities of the R set of genes or to changes in the condition of the S genes?

preted in chemical terms, but the simplest explanation is perhaps to suppose that it depends on changes in the proteins combined with the DNA; only when the DNA has the right protein attached to it is the regulator protein able to control the DNA's activity, either by removing the normal protein or in some other way.

Studies are still being very actively made to try to get nearer to the crucial points in the embryonic switch mechanisms at which particular genes or groups of genes are brought into activity. Many of the substances that were first shown to be very active in bringing about induction have their first effects on the cytoplasm, and certainly do not directly impinge on the genes. Some of the "metabolic" treatments probably have their first effect on the yolk granules, others on the external membrane of the cells.

At the present time the most active studies on embryonic evocators are concerned with substances that control the subtler variations in the result of induction. One can prepare from adult tissues some substances that, when placed in contact with an isolated piece of ectoderm, induce in it neural tissue which develops into the front part of the brain containing the eyes, other substances that tend to induce the middle and hinder parts of the brain opposite the ears, or again substances that tend to induce the spinal cord, or still others that induce only the somites and other mesodermal organs of the trunk and no neural tissue at all. It is generally thought now that these different end organs are the result of the induction of only two different types of tissue—namely, neural tissue and mesoderm. If only neural tissue is induced, it develops into the front part of the brain, the region of the body where in the normal embryo very little mesoderm is present. If the induction results in a mixture of a certain amount of the neural tissue and another quantity of mesoderm, then these two by self-individuation mold themselves into a part of the nervous system appropriate to that ratio of the two components. We are, therefore, probably dealing with the switching on of two different sets of genes, one controlling the formation of nerve proteins and the other the formation of mesoderm proteins. The evocating substances extracted from adult tissues are, when they are first isolated, compounds of nucleic acid and proteins. Further studies have suggested that the protein part is really the more important. It may be therefore that these studies are beginning to lead us toward a group of genotropic regulatory proteins, of a kind one would rather expect to be present on analogy with the bacterial situation discussed on pages 60–62. However, it is too early yet to say whether we are being too optimistic in this hope.

Another question one could ask is, what is the nature of the influence that emanates from the infolding mesoderm cells in the *normal* egg and affects the overlying ectoderm? This need not necessarily be the actual genotropic regulator which goes to the genes in the ectoderm cells and brings them into activity; it might be something quite different which unmasks the evocator already present in the ectoderm. We have at present no real answer to this question in connection with the neural induction in the amphibian egg. We are somewhat nearer an answer in relation to another inductive process, that by which parts of the neural tube at a later stage induce the mesoderm around them to form cartilage which is the beginning of the vertebral skeleton. Here there is very good evidence that the inducing neural tissue gives out a substance that is responsible for inducing the cartilage formation. The substance seems to be a fairly simple carbohydrate. It is difficult to imagine that this is specific enough to switch on the particular genes leading to the formation of cartilage substances. Most probably, therefore, it is acting on an already present specific regulatory substance within the cells competent to develop into cartilage.

The general picture that emerges from all this is that the embryonic cell is rather like a room where a cocktail party is going on with a radio set with press-button tuning in the center of it. The switching on of a particular battery of genes, controlling the synthesis, say, of nerve proteins, corresponds to pressing one particular button which brings in a program precisely from one station. But you may succeed in getting this button pressed by jogging the elbow of somebody at the other side of the room, who stumbles against the next man, and so on down the line until somebody finally falls against the radio set, and this may be sufficient to click on whichever of the tuning buttons is most insecure. (Changes in the competence of the cells would correspond to changes in the ease with which the tuning relays could be tripped.) Similarly, many influences impinging on competent embryonic cells may produce inductions, without revealing anything essential about the fundamental mechanisms controlling the underlying gene activities.

CHAPTER

5

Morphogenesis

DEVELOPING EMBRYOS CHANGE not only in chemical nature but also very obviously in their morphology. This term includes not only their external overall shape, which alters from a usually spherical egg to some more complicated structure with head, leg, tail, and so on, but also the disposition of all their various internal structures in space. The general name for the processes by which these spatial alterations are brought about is "morphogenesis." They must involve the action of forces that move parts of the embryo from one position to another. Explanations of morphogenesis have, therefore, to go beyond purely chemical considerations and give an account of the nature of these forces and show how they arise.

Shapes of Single Cells

What controls the shape of a single isolated cell? Consider first its general external shape. A cell consists of a small mass of cytoplasm enclosed within a membrane. The cell membrane usually has some tendency to contract, and when this is the case one would expect the cell, other things being equal, to assume the shape of a sphere, since this is the form in which the external surface of a mass is smallest and the membrane can therefore be most fully contracted. Many egg cells, in fact, do have a more or less spherical shape. When the egg cleaves into two, four, and more cells, these usually fit together into groups in which the individual cells again have the shape that would be expected for masses of material enclosed within contracting membranes. These shapes are, in fact, similar to those taken by groups of soap bubbles, which are masses of air enclosed within contracting soap films.

This is, however, only the very beginning of the story. For one thing it leaves out of account the arrangement of the internal contents of the cell. In the amphibian egg, as we have seen, the contents are not uniformly distributed, but the yolk is arranged in the form of a gradient, being more concentrated at the lower vegetative end. In this case the explanation—or at least part of it—is not difficult to see. The yolk gradient is certainly related to gravity, since when the egg is turned upside down, the heavy yolk streams down to the now lower end.

Gravity is certainly not the only factor. We saw (page 72) that a gray crescent appears at one side of the egg and that some special quality located at a particular region on the egg surface plays a part in bringing the crescent into this position. Therefore, the cell membrane is not a simple uniform contracting membrane. It has different properties in its different parts. This is also true in the sea urchin egg, where the two gradients, from animal to vegetative and from vegetative to animal, seem also to be located in the cell membrane. We have mentioned the fact that when eggs are centrifuged so that the internal contents are displaced, these materials tend to move back into their original arrangement, and it seems that the cell membrane is important in directing this rearrangement.

However, even in such comparatively simple structures as egg cells, it is difficult to attribute the entire morphology to the action merely of gravity and differences in different parts of the cell membrane. For instance, in the eggs of Ascidia (sea squirts) there are a number of slightly different colored regions of cytoplasm, and around the time of fertilization one can see that these carry out an elaborate series of movements (Figure 5·1). It is very difficult to account for all these movements in terms of gravity and membrane characteristics. It seems almost certain that some other forces arising within the body of the cytoplasm itself must be involved.

The fact that such forces do arise within cells, and can move the cytoplasm from place to place, is perhaps most strikingly shown in plant cells. In these the cytoplasm is often in constant movement, round and round in a kind of circular movement, referred to as "cyclosis." The forces that bring about this movement are still very mysterious, but we must accept it as a fact that forces can arise within the cytoplasm of cells and influence the position of the various regions in space.

In accounting for the shapes of the more complicated cells found in adult organisms we can, therefore, appeal to three types of factors: the cell surface, such general forces as gravity, and the internally arising cytoplasmic forces. It is the first and last of these that are usually most important, since it is only a few particularly heavy cellular components, such as yolk granules, that are much affected by gravity.

The relative importance of the cell surface and of the internal forces varies in different types of cells. In some unicellular organisms, such as ciliate protozoa, the surface is the predominant feature. In these organisms it has an elaborate structure, containing a large number of structures known as "kineties," each of which consists of a thread associated with a series of granules from which hairlike projections, the cilia, arise. Experiments have shown two

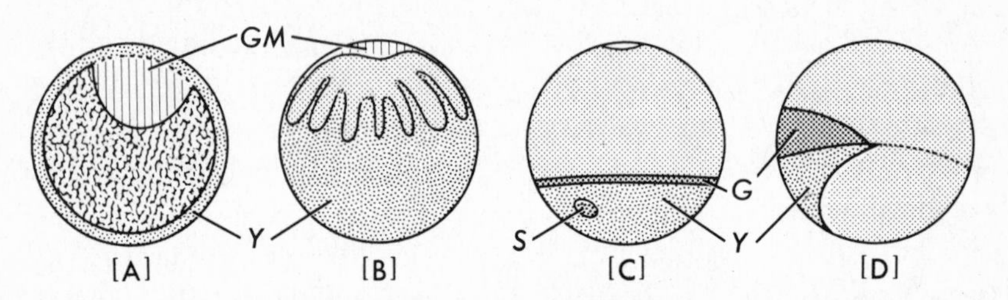

Figure 5·1. Movements of the cell contents after fertilization in ascidians. A: Just before fertilization, showing the germinal vesicles (GM) and the whole egg covered by a peripheral layer of yellow cytoplasm (Y). B: Immediately after fertilization, this streams down toward the vegetative pole. C: Shortly after this a gray layer (G) forms above the yellow (*S* is the position of the sperm nucleus). D: The gray and yellow regions then move up again onto one side to form two crescents.

important points. First, grafting parts of the cell surface from one region to another has shown that it is the surface with its contained kinetics which controls the general shape of the cell and influences profoundly the distribution of the internal contents. Second, it has been discovered that when the structure of the cell surfaces is altered into an abnormal pattern, this pattern may be copied exactly in the daughter cells and passed on in this way through many generations. The cell surface in these animals is, in fact, capable of controlling the pattern of the new surface formed when the cell reproduces itself. It is therefore not under the immediate control of the genes, since, if it were, it would be remodeled when cell division takes place.

There are probably few other types of cells in which the cell surface plays such an important role as it does in the ciliate protozoa. There are also few other cases in which the surface is so specialized and contains such elaborate structures. However, in many adult cells the surface certainly has considerable importance in determining the shape. For instance, a great many cells are polarized, in the sense that they have one end different from the other. A rather extreme case of this is the nerve cell, in which one end is drawn out to a long fiber, the axon, while the other, the dendrite, has a shorter, more branched shape. Such polarizations, which are usually less extreme than in nerves, are probably mainly determined by the cell surface. In many cases the surface properties concerned with polarity are not permanent. If we watch an isolated vertebrate cell in tissue culture we will see it moving for a time in one direction, with one end leading and the other trailing behind (see Figure 3·9). However, after a time this polarity lapses, and the cell may move off in another direction with a new part of its surface taking the leading position. Even when such surface-determined polarities are in operation, they are not the only factors that affect the cells' morphology. There is always some influence—stronger in some cases, weaker in others—of the internally arising forces, which influence the position of the nucleus and the various internal particles of the cell.

Small Groups of Cells

The shapes of individual cells are, of course, only rather minor details in the whole problem of morphogenesis in developing embryos. In general animal organs consist of many cells. We shall deal first with organs that, at the time they first acquire their fundamental shape, are built of relatively small numbers of cells; and later we shall discuss those in which even the first rudiments contain a large number. In the former category we may hope to explain the morphogenesis in terms of the ways in which the individual cells adhere to one another. In the latter so many cells are involved that this sort of explanation does not seem very likely to meet the case.

In very general terms, one may say that most cells tend to stick to one another in the conditions found in the living body. However, different types of cells exhibit rather different properties in the readiness with which they will adhere to others of their own or other kinds. Embryonic organs can often be broken down into their individual cells by treatments that leave the cells still alive and able to continue developing. This cellular disaggregation can be produced by some enzyme treatments, which destroy intercellular substances that normally hold the cells together. In many tissues calcium ions are important for cell adhesion, and if these are removed from the medium the cells tend to fall apart. When such disaggregated cells are kept in culture, and provided with essential substances such as calcium, they usually at first move about in a rather random fashion but eventually come together into groups.

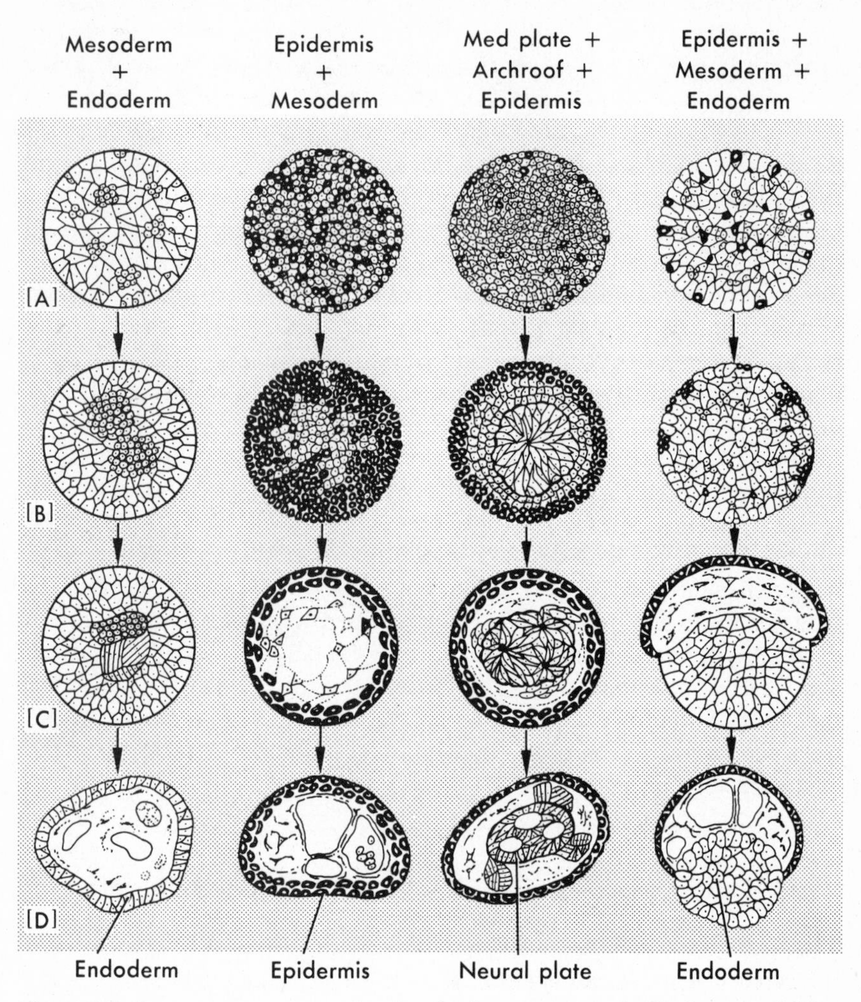

Figure 5·2. Rearrangements occurring in mixed aggregates of cells from amphibian neurula.

If cells of different kinds are mixed—or instance, cells from different species or from different organs of the same species—it is usual to find that the new aggregates that are formed at first contain a haphazard mixture of all possible types, but that after a time the various types become more or less sorted out. We cannot yet foretell, without doing the experiment, how far this sorting out will go. For instance, if one mixes together disaggregated cells from the embryonic liver and kidney of the chick and similar cells from the embryonic organs of the mouse, the cells sort themselves out according to the organ they come from, the liver cells sticking to liver cells and kidney cells to kidney cells. The difference between the species apparently has no effect, so that we get little kidney or liver aggregates in which mouse and chicken cells are intimately in contact with one another. If, however, the same experiment is done with amphibian embryos, the sorting out is primarily by the species, and the organ of origin plays a lesser although still quite important role.

In such mixed aggregates the various regions that become sorted out are not always arranged purely by chance. In experiments in which disaggregated amphibian embryonic cells are mixed there is a good deal of regularity both in the way the cells of similar kind became arranged into tissues and also in the general positions these tissues take up in the whole mass (Figure 5·2). For instance, ectoderm (epidermal or neural) cells and endoderm cells will both tend to form rather coherent sheets which are large in area and fairly thin in thickness, whereas mesoderm cells tend to be arranged in looser clusters of a roughly globular or thick form. In mixed cultures, containing mesoderm and either of the sheet-forming types (ectoderm or endoderm), the latter eventually appears at the surface and forms a sort of skin around the more solid core of mesoderm. If all three types are mixed together, then it is the ectoderm that forms the external skin (as in the normal embryo), while the sheet of endoderm becomes embedded within the mesoderm and usually rounds up into a number of tubules or vesicles near the center of the mass.

Morphogenesis of Tissues

The formation of a flat sheet or a solid mass of cells depends on the type of contact the cells make with one another. In a sheet each cell is only in contact with other cells over part of its surface, which one may call its sides, while other parts of its surface—that is, the two ends—remain exposed to the external medium. In a solid mass most of the cells, except those at the surface of the lump, are in contact with other cells all over. We still do not know why some cells establish intercellular contacts over the whole surface while others restrict this to certain parts only. The whole nature of intercellular contacts is very actively under investigation. The electron microscope has recently shown us that some cell contacts involve the formation of specialized areas on the cell surfaces, which form "attachment bodies" or "desmosomes." These are usually particularly well developed in cells in which the contact is confined to the sides, so that the sheetlike or epithelial arrangement is produced (Figure 5·3).

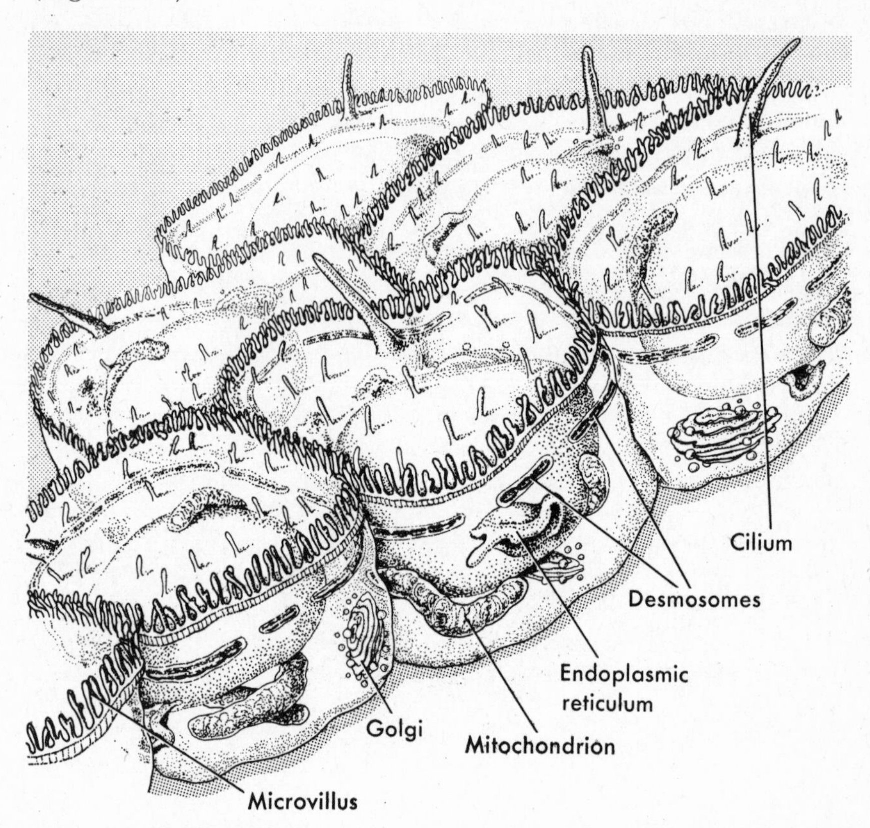

Figure 5·3. Diagram of cells of the chick embryo epidermis showing structures revealed by the electron microscope. In this type of cell, the desmosomes run all round the periphery of each cell.

Many of the earlier embryonic structures consist of such epithelia—for instance, the walls of the blastula, which fold into the three fundamental layers of ectoderm, mesoderm, and endoderm. Now if in an epithelium the area of contact between adjacent cells is changed, the whole epithelium may become folded or otherwise altered in shape. This is illustrated in Figure 5.4. It is most probable that changes of this kind are very important in bringing about some of the first phases of morphogenesis in many embryos.

The early development of the sea-urchin egg provides a good example of morphogenesis produced by the combined operations of selective cell adhesion and cell polarity (see Figure 1·1, page 2). During the stages of cleavage the cells adhere to one another over relatively small areas, and they also stick to the membrane that surrounds the whole egg. These two factors are enough to account for the formation of the blastula as a hollow sphere. The first sign of gastrulation is a thickening and flattening of the lower vegetative portion of this sphere. This change is brought about by an increase in the area of contact between the cells in this region—their sides become larger in area and their ends smaller.

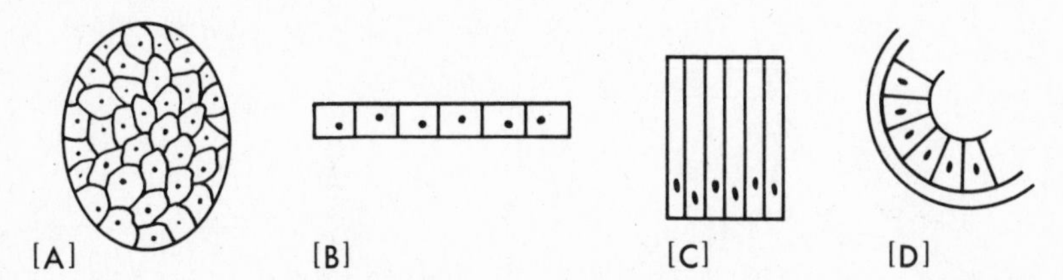

Figure 5·4. Shapes of cells and tissues. A: Diagram of a section through a solid mass of tissue; most of the cells are in contact with other cells over their whole surface. **B:** A row of six cells forming part of a flat epithelium. If the area of contact between the cells increases, the whole epithelium may become much thicker and the cells more elongated as in **C.** If the lower side of the cells is attached to a basement membrane so that this region cannot decrease in area while the area of contact between the sides increases, then the whole epithelium will be bent into an arc, as in **D.**

We then begin to see obvious signs of polarity in these cells. Their outer ends, toward the external medium, become still smaller, while their inner ends tend to enlarge and to push out in the form of pseudopodia. This leads, in the first place, to a sudden bending inward of this region, which is the beginning of the invagination of the primitive gut. The formation of pseudopodia by the inner faces of these cells becomes very active. Some of the cells in fact creep right out of the layer and lie free within the internal cavity of the blastula. These are the first cells of the mesoderm. At first they lie in a more or less haphazard arrangement throughout the greater part of the internal cavity, but they gradually settle down into a ring fitting close up against the ectoderm somewhat below the equator; this seems to be due to a selectively greater adhesiveness between the mesoderm cells and the ectoderm in this region. Meanwhile the pseudopodia from the cells still remaining in the external wall of the infolding primitive gut reach out long processes right across the internal cavity. These processes adhere preferentially to the inner surfaces of the cells at the diametrically opposite pole of the blastula. When they make contact with these cells the pseudopodia seem to become anchored fast to them, and they then contract, thus pulling the vegetative end of the blastula further inward until it forms a deep pocket pushed into the interior of the original blastula cavity. In this way the embryo is converted into a three-layered gastrula, and the fundamentally important morphogenetic event of gastrulation has been brought about.

Gastrulation in the amphibian egg involves some of the same principles but also brings into play another type of process which is very important in many embryos but is still difficult to understand. As in the sea urchin, cleavage leads to the formation of a hollow blastula, presumably because the cells adhere to one another only

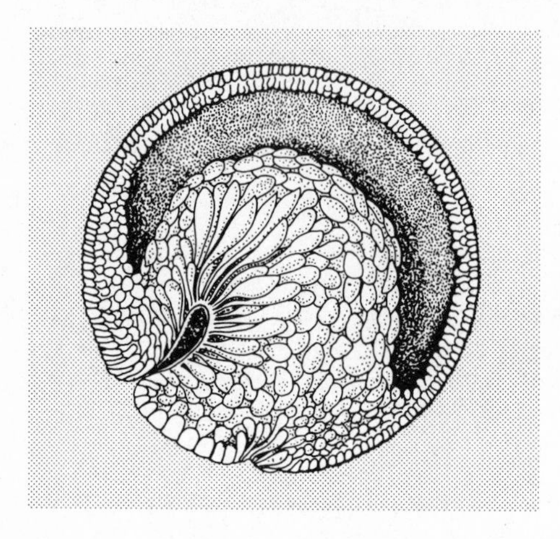

Figure 5·5. Diagram of one side of a newt gastrula showing the shape of cells in the interior.

over relatively small areas of their surface. The gastrulation again starts with the intucking of a small area to form the blastopore. This appears not at the most vegetative pole, where the cells are very large and yolky and rather inactive, but somewhat above it on the dorsal side. The intucking is produced by polar activity of the cells in this region; their outer surfaces become very small, while their inner surfaces become large and tend to be free of contact with other cells, so that the whole of their cell body becomes drawn out into a sort of pear-shaped object (Figure 5·5).

At this time, however, a new phenomenon appears. The whole epithelial layer that forms the surface of the blastula just above the blastopore begins to elongate along the direction of the dorsal axis and at the same time to become narrower from side to side. If one makes a series of marks with a vital dye across the dorsal axis in this region, the marked cells are seen to stream down toward the blastopore and to come closer together in the midline (Figure 5·6). Since the region of the blastopore has already been pulled a little inward by the polar behavior of the cells there, as described above, these streams become directed into the interior of the blastula, so

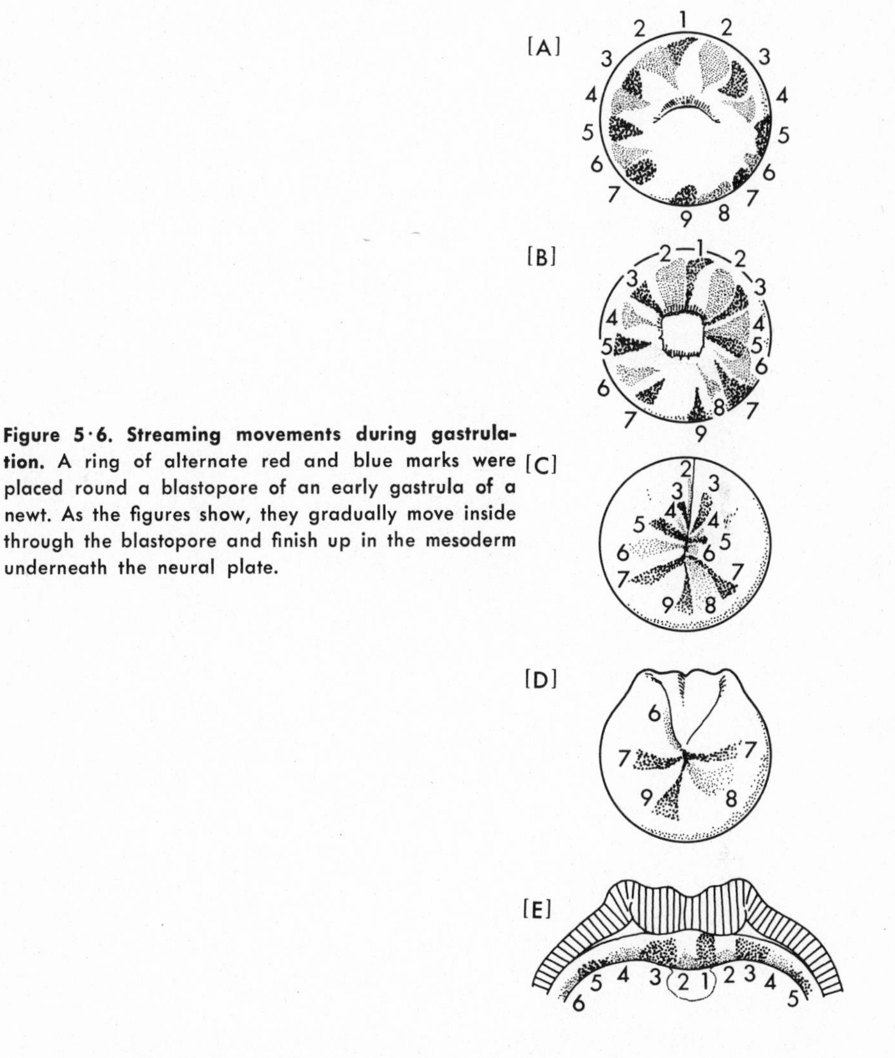

Figure 5·6. Streaming movements during gastrulation. A ring of alternate red and blue marks were placed round a blastopore of an early gastrula of a newt. As the figures show, they gradually move inside through the blastopore and finish up in the mesoderm underneath the neural plate.

that they give rise to a tube leading inward, which becomes the primitive gut and develops into both the mesoderm and the endoderm. If the egg is kept in a medium with somewhat abnormal osmotic pressure, the polar behavior of the blastopore cells may be partially suppressed, and in this case the cell streams are not pulled inward, but simply elongate to give rise to an excrescence sticking outward from the blastopore region. Such a formation is known as an exogastrula. The ectoderm and endoderm cells that should have got into the interior of the egg now differentiate lying nakedly in the medium. Meanwhile the ectoderm, which has no

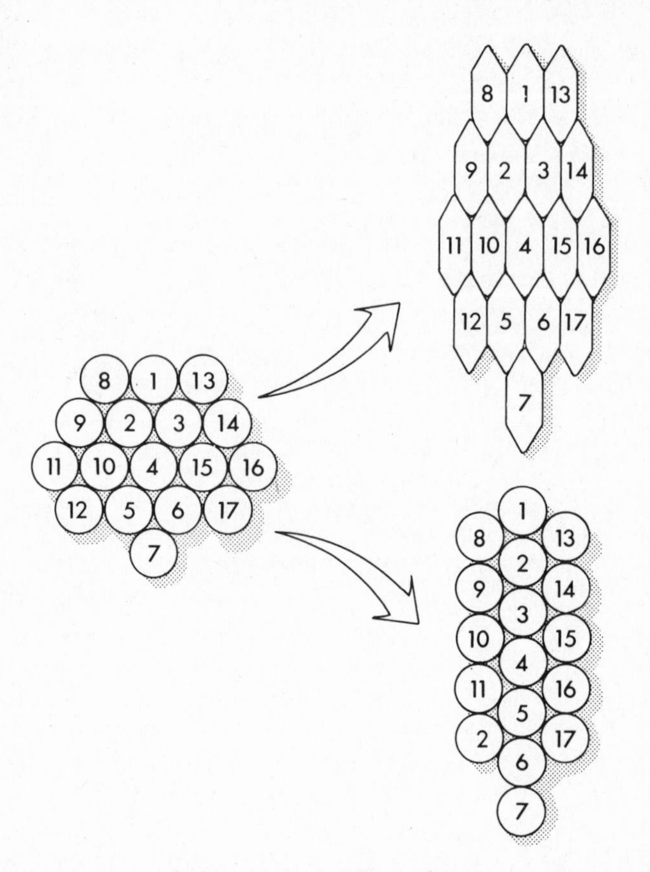

Figure 5·7. Two ways in which a group of cells could become longer and narrower. Above, by changing the shape of the cells without altering their arrangement; this certainly does not happen during amphibian gastrulation. But if each cell had two definite regions of attachment (for example, two desmosome positions), the group might become rearranged, as shown below, without any change in cell shape.

mesoderm lying in contact with it as usual, does not become acted on by the neural inducer and fails to develop into the nervous system. This is one of the clearest demonstrations of the importance of induction in normal development.

The mechanism of the cell streams is still very obscure. It certainly involves some sort of polarity within the cells. If a piece of the material that is just beginning to elongate is cut out and rotated and placed back in a new orientation, it tends to go on elongating in its original direction, and this must be a sign of an inherent polarity. However, the individual cells do not change their shape much during the process and certainly do not elongate as much as the whole mass. Movement must therefore involve the cells releasing contact with one another and making new contact. It may be that no more is involved than specially adhesive regions of the cells, arranged in a polar way so that the cells can get lined up end to end into a narrow strand (Figure 5·7). However, streaming movements of this kind are found in many embryos, and often occur, for instance in the chick embryo, in regions that contain many hundred cells packed together in thick layers. Here it seems rather less likely that the behavior is to be explained in terms of the properties of the individual cells. It looks rather as though some force is arising within the cell mass as a whole, more or less independently of its division into the separate cells, and having little to do with the properties of the cell surfaces.

Multicellular Organs

In the later stages of development, most organs consist of such large numbers of cells that an explanation of morphogenesis in terms of the properties of cell surfaces becomes difficult to imagine. As one example let us consider the formation of the bony skeleton of the vertebrate limb. This skeleton consists of one bone in the upper part of the limb (upper arm or thigh), two bones in the lower part (lower arm or leg), then a series of small bones forming the wrist and ankle joints, and finally a number of fingers or toes, typically five. In embryonic development, the limb first appears as a small collection of mesoderm cells, which accumulate to form small lumps at the appropriate places on the flank of the embryo. It is still rather obscure what causes them to accumulate in normal development; but if an accumulation of mesoderm is brought about at an abnormal position by inserting some unusual structure (for example, a nose vesicle or even an inert lump, such as a piece of celloidin) into the side of an embryo, a new extra limb may grow out of it. It seems therefore that it is the initial collection of mesoderm cells that sets off the whole process of limb development.

One of the first things that happens is that the polarity of the limb becomes determined. This can be tested by cutting out the limb bud and rotating it before placing it back again. It is then found that at a very early stage the anterior-posterior polarity of the lump of material becomes fixed, so that if it is reversed the limb develops with its front side (that is, that carrying the thumb or the big toe) pointing backward (Figure 5·8). However, at this stage the dorsal-ventral polarity is not yet fixed, and the limb bud can be rotated in such a way as to reverse it, and still the limb will develop with the back of the hand and the palm in the right positions relative to the body as the whole. It is only at a slightly later stage that this dorsoventral polarity also becomes determined, and the third axis, that leading from the trunk out toward the extremities, is determined even later, so that by suitable reversals the part that should normally turn into the thigh can be converted into the toes till quite a late stage. We still have absolutely no clue of the physiochemical nature of these polarities, or whether they are properties of individual cells or of whole tissue masses.

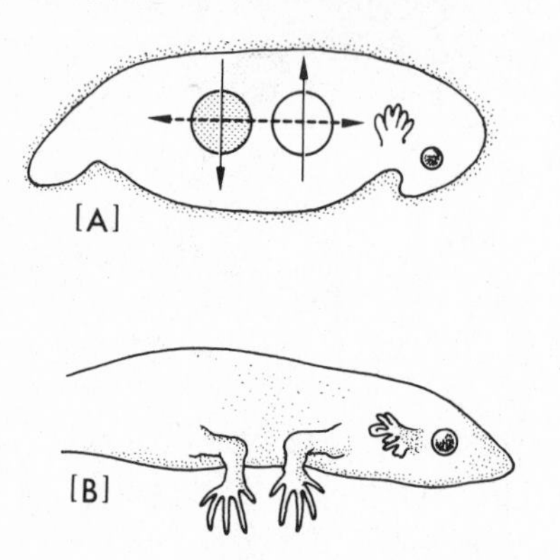

Figure 5·8. Tissue polarity in limb buds. A: A limb bud from another embryo has been grafted into the flank of a newt embryo just posterior to the normal limb bud. The graft has been rotated so that both its dorsoventral axis (solid line) and anteroposterior axis (dotted line) are reversed in direction. **B:** In the limb that develops, the dorsoventral axis has been changed into conformity with the host, but the limb has reversed anteroposterior orientation.

In the establishment of the pattern of bones within the limb an important role is played by the ectoderm, although, of course, the bones themselves appear within the mesoderm (Figure 5·9). Shortly after the mesoderm cells aggregate into a sizable limb bud, a thickened ridge appears in the ectoderm that covers this little swelling. It is particularly well seen in embryos of birds and mammals and is referred to as the apical ridge. It seems to come into being under the influence of the mesoderm, and some influences from the mesoderm are probably necessary to keep it in being. It is the ridge, however, that is responsible for determining the pattern of condensations within the limb mesoderm that will finally develop into the bones. If part of the ridge is removed, the limb appears with an incomplete bony pattern—perhaps only two fingers instead of five. Again if the ectoderm is stripped off a leg bud and is replaced with ectoderm containing the ridge taken from an arm bud, then the leg mesoderm develops not with the leg pattern but with the pattern of the arm. Presumably there must be substances diffusing from the apical ridge into the mesoderm, and vice versa, and also substances diffusing from place to place within the mesoderm mass, and in some way these substances cause the cells to begin to aggregate more tightly in the places where the bones are going to develop; but we still know nothing about the nature of the substances or any details of their action.

The formation of the limb skeleton is only one example, chosen out of an enormous number, in which a mass of embryonic developing tissue becomes molded or "individuated" into a specific pattern and shape. We might have chosen almost any other organ of the body as an illustration. Unfortunately they all would remain equally

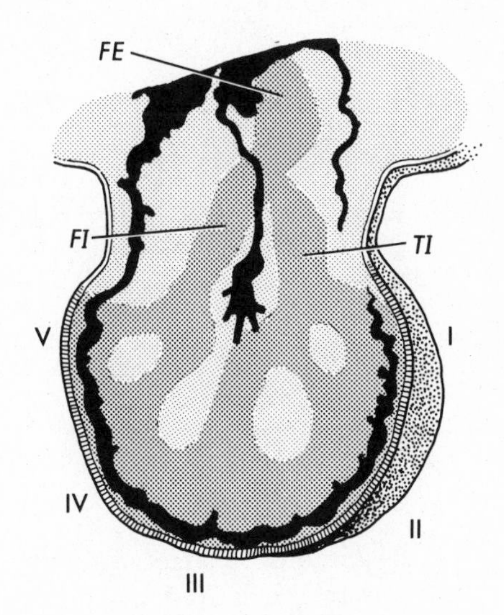

Figure 5·9. A young limb bud of the mouse. The apex of the bud is clothed with thickened ectoderm (the "apical ridge"). The mesoderm inside is beginning to condense into more tightly packed regions which will become the five digits (*I* to *V*), the tibia and fibula (*TI* and *FI*), and the femur (*FE*). The blood vessels are shown in black.

mysterious. We can, of course, often show that different parts of the developing mass are influencing one another. For instance, as the eye gradually acquires its final form there are interactions between the retina and the lens. If the normal lens is removed and a larger one substituted, then the retinal part of the eye grows extra large, or the lens itself grows rather more slowly so that a more or less normally proportioned eye results. Again, as the neural tube, which originally has a more or less uniform diameter tapering off slightly toward the posterior, gradually develops into the brain with a series of large swellings toward the front end, there are interactions between it and the surrounding mesoderm and other tissues (Figure 5·10). In all cases in which the final organ has a complicated pattern, there are in fact many interactions between

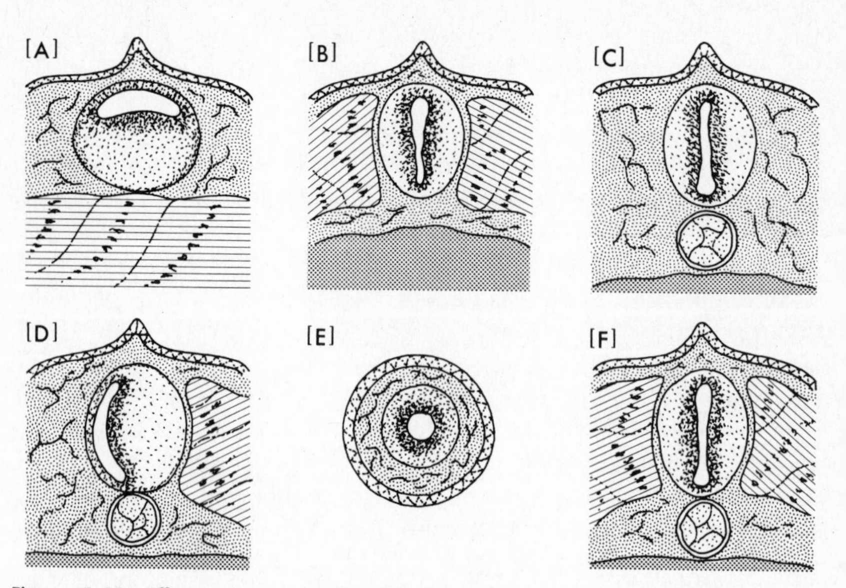

Figure 5·10. Effects of surrounding tissues (muscles, notochord, mesenchyme) on the shape of the neural tube in amphibia.

all the different parts. The whole system must be a sort of complicated crossfire, in which each part influences every other part.

We have still no notion of the physicochemical mechanisms of these interactions, and the best we can do is to refer to the whole complex of them as a "morphogenetic field." The word "field" is used with a rather vague reminiscence of its use in the physical sciences, where one speaks of an electromagnetic field, a diffusion field, and so on. In embryology we have still no idea what it is a field *of*. We use the word only to mean that throughout a certain mass of developing tissue there is some generally pervasive influence that relates the various parts so that they fit together into an organized pattern. This is really no more than a description of what we see and can demonstrate in experiment. It is not in any sense an explanation of the events, because we cannot say what the agents that exert this pervasive influence are. Probably, in fact, there is no one single type of agent. It is more likely that a whole series of different factors—specific adhesiveness between different cell types, diffusion of substances out from the periphery of the mass, accumulation of other substances in its central parts, cell polarities, and perhaps many other aspects of cell physiology that we do not yet understand—combine to give rise to the organized patterns we see gradually developing.

After the rudiments of the various organs have acquired their basic structure, their shape and the shape of the embryo as a whole are often considerably changed by differences in the rates at which the various parts grow. The general subject of growth is too large to be treated fully here. It is one of the most important aspects of cell biology and of the general biology of the organism. We shall be able to mention only one or two general principles.

It is rare to find that all parts of an organism are growing at the same rate. Nearly always a particular organ is growing either faster or slower than the body as a whole. In many cases the relation between the growth of a part and of the whole can be expressed, to a first approximation at least, in a simple mathematical form. If x is the magnitude (weight or volume) of a whole organism and y that of some part of it, it is often found that the relation between these two at different stages of the life history fits very nearly to the equation $y = bx^a$. If a is larger than 1, then the organ is growing faster than the whole body, so that as the animal grows the organ gets disproportionately larger and larger. If a is less than 1, then as growth proceeds the organ will progressively become relatively smaller compared to the whole animal. Growth that takes place according to this rule is often referred to as allometric growth. In the growth of the human body (Figure 5·11)

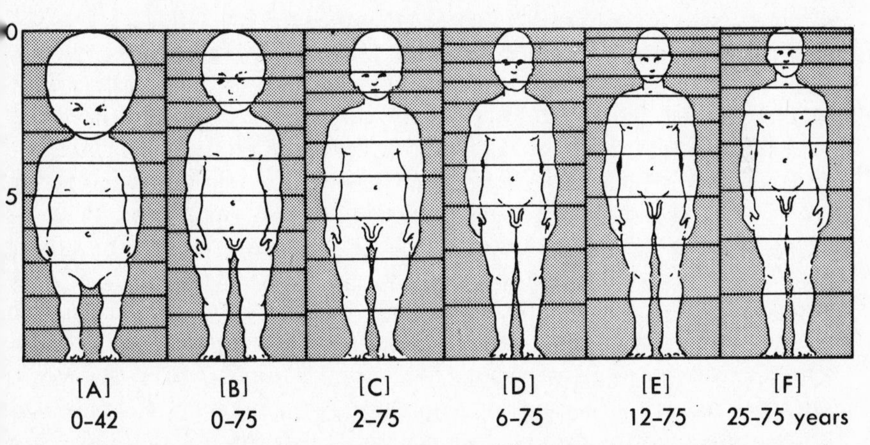

Figure 5·11. Changes in form of the human male body, due to relative growth. The outline of the body has been reduced to the same height to emphasize the changes in proportions independently of absolute sizes.

the legs grow with positive allometry and the head with negative allometry, the former becoming proportionately larger and the latter proportionately smaller as life proceeds.

As this figure illustrates, it is rather artificial to consider the body as made up of quite separate organs that grow independently of one another. In fact, all parts of the body are related to one another in their growth rates. We really have to deal, not with separate organs, each with its own growth rate, but rather with continuous gradients in growth rate, which vary gradually from one part of the body to the next. For instance, in Figure 5·11 it is clear that the uppermost part of the skull has a smaller growth coefficient than the lower part.

The factors controlling these growth gradients are perhaps better understood in plants than in animals. In plants it has been shown that a growing meristem gives out hormones that affect the growth rate of meristems in the neighborhood, usually by reducing it. A whole series of such hormones and hormone-like substances are known, often connected with the response of the plant to the length of daylight to which it is exposed. By manipulating these hormones botanists have been able to obtain considerable control over the form of the growing plant.

In animals the factors controlling the growth gradients are less well understood. It is certain that hormones are often involved, but there must be other, more localized agents that also come into play. It is clear also that genetic factors are fundamentally important, as is obvious when one considers the differences in size and shape of the various races, for instance, of domestic dogs. Although the nature of the factors controlling the fields of growth gradients in animals are so mysterious, the fields themselves are fundamentally important, not only for the growth of healthy animals but particularly in relation to disease. It is an unfortunate fact that cells, of both animals and plants, sometimes suffer alterations that cause them to start growing and dividing more rapidly than they should. Such abnormal growths are known as tumors, and when the growing cells, in addition, show a tendency to break loose from their original location and move to other parts of the body, the tumors are said to become "malignant." Such tumors often interfere with the proper working of the organs of the body and are then known as cancers. We cannot discuss here the complicated and still obscure question of the nature of the changes that cause cells to become cancerous. The point to be noticed in the present connection is that one of the most basic and one of the most dangerous characteristics of cancerous cells is that they break loose from the control of the growth fields that control the normal development of the body. A fuller understanding of the nature of these fields would therefore be extremely relevant to an understanding of, and possibly even to the control of, cancerous growth. It is probably significant that it is rather rare to find cancers occurring in animal organs that are "good at" regeneration, such as the limbs of newts. Some authors have indeed claimed that if fragments of tumor tissue are placed in a regenerating newt limb, the powerful growth fields that must be controlling the growth of the regenerating material can also keep in check the growth of the cancer cells.

DEGENERATION AND SENESCENCE

One is perhaps often tempted to think of embryonic development only as a positive process, which leads from the egg to the adult and then stops. However, the adult form of an animal, although relatively long-lasting compared to any of the embryonic stages, is not a completely static and unchanging state; it is altering slightly all the time and finally shows signs of old age and eventually dies. The study of aging should really be looked upon as a part of embryology, but it is a somewhat separate field, as is the study of growth, and there is space here to mention it only very briefly.

The signs of senescence or old age are manifold and difficult to define precisely. Many different organs of the body become less efficient, and the organism as a whole becomes subject to many different types of disease. The most obvious outcome of the whole process is, of course, that the animal dies. It may do this for a large number of different, particular reasons, but the overall picture is that everything is getting less effective and less resistant to breakdown, until finally something gives way and the animal's life is terminated. Many of the studies of the aging process are in fact carried out by taking a population of animals and ascertaining the ages at which the various individuals die "of natural causes."

It is the general observation that animals that cannot control their body temperature die after a shorter time when they have lived at a high temperature than when they have lived at a low. This is what we should expect if the degenerative processes are brought about by normal chemical actions, which go faster at high temperatures. However, it does not seem to be the case that there is some general "death process" going on all the time at a rate that is increased by high temperatures. If this were so, an animal that was kept for a considerable time at a high temperature, and then transferred to a lower one, would have its expectation of life at that low temperature considerably reduced. The experimental result is that such animals survive at the low temperature for just about as long as animals that are kept in the low temperature all their lives. It seems that the processes leading to senescence go on throughout life at a rate that is more or less independent of temperature. The reason why animals die earlier at high temperature is simply that the hotter conditions are more demanding, so that an animal that is only slightly senescent is no longer tough enough to put up with them.

In these days of atomic energy and bomb fallout, it is an important fact that ionizing radiations tend to shorten the life-span. Such radiations also cause mutations. One of the theories of senescence that has had considerable support is the idea that the aging process is due to the occurrence of gene mutations in the cells of the body. Most such mutations would be harmful in their effects, and it might be that gradual accumulation of a large number of slightly harmful mutations causes the cells to become less efficient in all sorts of different ways. It seems most probable, in fact, that this is how the life-shortening effect of ionizing radiation comes about. However, it is by no means certain that the normal aging process is also due to gene mutations. If it were, we should expect that animals with only one of each type of chromosome ("haploids") would age much more rapidly than similar animals that have two of each kind of chromosome ("diploids"), since in the latter there are two representatives of each gene and the effect of mutations in one of these two would be largely concealed by the actions of the complementary gene. One can test this in animals like bees and wasps. In these the males are normally haploid, but by special breeding it is possible to produce diploid males. It turns out that these diploids have no great advantage over the haploids in length of life under normal conditions. They are, however, very much more resistant to the life-shortening effects of radiation, which supports the idea that this effect is due to the induction of mutations.

It looks, therefore, as though normal aging and radiation-induced aging may be brought about by rather different processes. Perhaps both of them affect in different ways the general processes of protein synthesis in cells. Certainly one would expect that random gene mutations would tend to slow down the formation of the normal proteins, and this would be likely to reduce the efficiency of the cells in carrying out their functions. The natural aging process could operate by affecting the mechanism of protein synthesis at some other point in the whole complicated machine which we described earlier (page 27).

It is as well to remember that the death of individual cells is taking place all through development. Even in the early embryo, in which most cells are growing and multiplying, one can nearly always find some similar cells that are dying, degenerating, and being resorbed. In many embryos there are whole organs, such as the notochord in the higher vertebrates, that appear in the embryo and may play an important role for some time, but then die and disappear long before the adult stage is reached.

Concluding Remarks

All aspects of embryonic development depend, in the last resort, on interactions between the genes in the nuclei and the medium—nuclear sap and cytoplasm—in which they are placed. These interactions are mutual, operating in both directions: the cytoplasm brings the genes into operation or represses them, and at the same time the activity of the genes changes the cytoplasm.

These gene-cytoplasm interactions can be studied, at the simplest level, in organisms such as bacteria, which can hardly be said to undergo development. The main fascination of the embryology of higher organisms is that it faces us squarely with the issue of biological organization, of end results that are definite and relatively simple emerging from systems that are enormously complicated and involve many hundreds of elementary genes. All the experimental approaches we have rapidly surveyed—to such problems as the entry of genes into activity in orderly succession as histogenesis proceeds, the switching of the developing system into a particular path by a particular type of cytoplasm or by an inductive interaction between neighboring cells, the cooperation of cells in morphogenesis, and so on—are methods by which biology is feeling its way toward solving this great problem of organization. We are certainly still far from understanding how developing systems are actually organized and the activities of so many separate genes integrated; and it will probably take us a long time before we have anything like a satisfactory picture of the situation. But perhaps we now see clearly what should be the next steps toward that goal. In my opinion, at least, the three problems immediately in front of us are these: What is the nature of the change that renders a cell competent, so that it is ready to be switched into a particular developmental path? What is it that triggers off the switch and puts the cell into a state of determination, which is only with difficulty reversible, and can normally be transmitted through several cell generations? Finally, how are the activities of all the genes concerned in any developmental pathway tied together, so that they proceed in an integrated and orderly manner—or does this, perhaps, follow from the answers to the first two questions? It seems certain that these answers, whatever they turn out to be, will have to center around the nature of the substances that go to, and modify the activity of, the genes—the genotropic substances. We still have absolutely no *certain* knowledge of what they are, in any single case. The betting is that they are allosteric proteins, but they might be allosteric RNA. In either case, although the heroes of the play, they have still kept tantalizingly offstage up to date.

Further Reading

GENERAL AND REFERENCE

There are many good and well-illustrated accounts of descriptive embryology. A. F. Huettner's *Fundamentals of Comparative Embryology of the Vertebrates* (New York: Macmillan, 1949) is very good in its field. L. G. Barth's *Embryology* (New York: Dryden Press, 1953) and V. Hamburger's *A Manual on Experimental Embryology* (Chicago: University of Chicago Press, 1947) are two excellent formal textbooks. For those who read German, O. Pflugfelder's *Entwicklungsgeschichte und Entwicklungsphysiologie der Tiere* (Jena: Fischer, 1962) gives a lavishly illustrated account of embryos in all groups, with summaries of the experimental analyses. The descriptive accounts given in the larger textbooks of experimental embryology will probably be sufficient for most purposes. Among the best and most recent of these books are: B. I. Balinsky, *An Introduction to Embryology* (Philadelphia: Saunders, 1960); B. H. Willier, P. A. Weiss, and V. Hamburger, *Analysis of Development* [mainly vertebrate] (Philadelphia: Saunders, 1955); A. Kühn, *Entwicklungsphysiologie* (Berlin: Springer, 1965); and C. H. Waddington, *Principles of Embryology* (London: Allen and Unwin, 1956). Only the last two of these devote much attention to the interpretation of developmental processes in terms of genetics.

Molecular biology is advancing so fast that there are no good and fully up-to-date texts. R. Sager and F. J. Ryan's *Cell Heredity* (New York: Wiley, 1961) is very good up to its date. G. H. Haggis, D. Michie, A. R. Muir, K. B. Roberts, and P. M. B. Walker's *Introduction to Molecular Biology* (London: Longmans, 1964) is the most recent extensive treatment.

For morphogenesis, J. T. Bonner provides a simple but widely based account in his *Morphogenesis* (Princeton, N.J.: Princeton University Press, 1952). E. W. Sinnott's *Plant Morphogenesis* (New York: McGraw-Hill, 1960) is a comprehensive treatise, and the same author's *The Problem of Organic Form* (New Haven, Conn.: Yale University Press, 1963) is a simpler discussion, again mainly, though not exclusively, about plants. C. H. Waddington's *New Patterns in Genetics and Development* (New York: Columbia University Press, 1962) deals only with animals but pays more attention to genetics and molecular biology than the others.

SPECIAL TOPICS

The International Review of Cytology (Vol. 15, 1963) has three useful but specialized articles: H. G. Callan's "The Nature of Lampbrush Chromosomes," J. L. Sirlin's "The Intracellular Transfer of Genetic Information," and T. Gustafson, and L. Wolpert's "The Cellular Basis of Morphogenesis and Sea-Urchin Development." *The American Zoologist* (Vol. 3, 1963) has a series of articles on various developmental biological topics.

Some articles at a rather simpler level are: J. T. Bonner, "The Unsolved Problem of Development," *Amer. Scientist,* 1960; M. Fischberg and A. W. Blackler, "How Cells Specialize," *Sc. Amer.,* 1961; E. H. Mercer, *Cells and Cell Structure* (London: Hutchinson Educational), 1961; T. R. Elsdale, "Cell Surgery," *Penguin Science Survey,* Vol. B, 1963; R. M. Clayton, "Differentiation," and J. Maynard-Smith, "The Causes of Ageing," both in *Penguin Science Survey,* Vol. B, 1964; R. Sager, "Genes Outside the Chromosomes," *Sc. Amer.,* January 1965; and J. B. Gurdon, "Nuclear Transplantation," *Quart. Rev. Biol.,* March 1963.

Index

For some commonly used words, references are given only to definitions or main discussions.

active sites, 43, 62, 86
ageing, 107
allometric growth, 105
allosteric proteins, 43, 62, 63, 86, 110
amphibia, 3, 4, 70–79
  constriction, 55, 72
  gastrulation, 4, 98
  RNA in, 30, 31
  regeneration, 52–54
animal-vegetative axis, 2, 3
annulate lamellae, 35
apical ridge, 102
arginine 41, 42
Aristotle, 14
Ascaris, 17
ascidians, 91, 92
asymmetry, 19, 20
autoradiography, 29
Avery, 24

Baer, von, 6
Beadle, 23
blastema, 52–54
blastopore, 3, 4, 73, 79, 86
blastula, 2, 72
blood cell, 37, 54, 59
Boveri, 16
Bridges, 17

cambium, 11
canalization 22, 47–50
cancer, 106
cartilage, 37, 89
cell
  adhesion, 93, 95, 97, 100
  differentiation, 37
  isolated, 9, 12, 76, 90–92
  membrane, 13, 47, 86, 90–93
  plant, 91
  shape, 90–93
  ultrastructure, 33, 96
chick embryo, 79–85
Chironomus, 65
chromosomes, 16, 17, 25, 34, 38, 62, 65, 87
  lampbrush, 36, 38
  salivary, 65, 68
ciliates, 63, 64, 92
cleavage, 2, 7, 17, 80
coding problem, 26
competence, 78, 79, 87
control mechanisms, 29, 31, 43, 59, 60, 61, 86
Crick, 25

cyclosis, 91
cytoplasmic genes, 35, 92

Darwin, 6
death, 107–109
dedifferentiation, 50, 54
desmosomes, 96, 100, 101
differentiation
  kinds of, 7, 8
  plants, 13
disaggregation, 93–94
DNA, 25, 26
dominance, 47
Drosophila
  bithorax, 20–22, 68
  wing, 45, 46

E. coli, 60
echinoderms (*see* sea urchin)
ectoderm, 4, 79
egg
  activation, 56
  cortex, 47, 71
  cytoplasm, 16–19, 36, 47, 71
endoderm, 4, 79, 80
endoplasmic reticulum, 32, 34
end-product inhibition, 43, 60
end-product repression, 60, 86
enzyme
  active sites, 43, 62, 86
  allosteric, 43, 62, 63, 80, 110
  constitutive, 62
  control, 43, 60, 86
  inactivation, 41, 43
  inhibition, 60
  networks, 42
  repression, 60
Ephrussi, 23
epigenesis, 14, 15
epigenetic landscape, 49, 50
  epigenetics, 15
evocation, 77, 79, 84–89
evolution, 5–7, 18, 22
exogastula, 100

feedback, 49
fertilization, 30, 31, 72, 91
  membrane, 2
fields, 104
flatworms, 53

galactosidase, 60
gastrulation, 2–5, 79, 97–99
germ cell determinants, 35
genotropic substances, 67, 68, 89
genes
  batteries of, 44, 63, 69, 87
  inactivation, 98
  operator, 61, 62
  regulator, 61
  structural, 23, 61
genetic code, 26
gill slits, 6
glycogen, 86
Goldschmidt, 23
golgi, 32
gradients, 2, 71, 84, 91, 105
gravity, 91
gray crescent, 71, 72
  growth, 9, 103, 105
  cells, 10, 12
  gradients, 106

Haeckel, 6
hemoglobin, 37, 39, 40, 54, 59
Hensen's node, 82
heterochromatin, 69
histogenesis, 8, 9
histones, 67
hormones, 66, 67, 106
hybridization, molecular, 29, 30

imaginal buds, 44
individuation, 77, 79, 80, 84, 103
inducers, enzymes, 61, 69
induction, 16, 74, 75, 76, 84, 85–8
  cartilage, 89
  indirect, 86
  secondary, 74, 75

lens, 52, 55, 78, 82, 103
life span, 108
limbs, 101, 102
  regeneration, 53, 54
Limnaea, 19, 20, 87
lysosomes, 35

man, 6, 105
masked evocator, 86

maternal effects, 68
McLeod, 24
meristem, 10, 11, 106
mesoderm, 4, 79, 80
metabolism of blastopore, 86
metaplasia, 12, 50, 54
mitochondria, 32, 35
Morgan, 17, 18, 19, 22
morphogenesis, 8, 9, 90
mosaic eggs, 16
Muller, 18
muscle cell, 37
myoglobin, 43

natural selection, 6, 40, 42, 48
neural crest, 3
neural plate, 3
neural tube, 104
Neurospora, 23, 41, 42
nonchromosomal genes, 35, 92
notochord, 5, 82, 84
nuclear differentiation, 56
nuclear envelope, 33, 34, 35
nuclear transplantation, 55–58
nucleic acids, 24–27
nucleolus, 30, 34, 73

one-gene-one-enzyme hypothesis, 23
oogenesis, 19
ooplasms, 16–19, 36, 47, 71
operon, 61
organizers, 75, 76, 85–89

Paramecium, 63, 64
penicillin, 60
phylogeny, 6
plants, 9–13
  plasticity, 12
polarity, 2, 93, 100–102
polysomes, 28, 32
position effect, 69, 70
preformation, 14, 15
primitive gut, 2
primitive streak, 81
proteins, 24–27, 39
puffs, 65, 66, 68, 69

reassortment
  cells, 94
  tissues, 95
recapitulation, 6
regeneration, 52–54, 107
regionalization, 8, 9, 88
regulation, 48–50
  of genes, 61, 79, 86–89
regulation eggs, 16
repressors, 62
reversibility, 50–52, 54
ribosomes, 28, 29, 32, 59, 73
RNA
  in embryos, 29–32, 73
  varieties, 26–28
root, 10, 11

sea urchin, 2, 5
  gradients, 91
  morphogenesis, 97
  RNA in, 30, 31
self-duplication, 25
senescence, 107, 108
sequences, 67, 68
shoot, 10, 11
sickle cell, 39
snails, 19, 87
somites, 4, 5, 82, 83
Spemann, 55
Sturtevant, 18, 19
switch mechanisms, 21, 50, 59, 68, 85–89

Tatum, 23
tissue, plant, 12
tissue culture, 50, 51, 74, 76
tissue movements, 73, 81, 82, 99, 100
transcription, 26, 31, 59, 63
transformation, 24
translation, 31, 59, 63
tumors, 106
twins, 48, 80

Watson, 25
Wilkins, 25

yolk, 34, 71, 79, 88, 91